RONDO ONE-EYE

List of Illustrations

*Prints of Illustrations Available From
Crowhill Books & Web Orderline*

Acknowledgements

Many good friends helped in a number of ways throughout the periods of writing and revising this book. Since I spent a good deal of that time an almost terminally impecunious condition, I'm more than happy to mention just a few of those who came to my aid.

My partner Sarah for putting up with the longest gestation of her career and trying to get me to stop smoking. Ray & Mary Norris and my sister, Fiona, for timely, sympathetic interventions. D.H. "The Brigadier", McNeill, for fivers, beer, fags and fun; K. McFarlane for letting me see (and feel the pain of) the north end of Coll from a bike with no saddle. Rosemary Griffin for providing typing, gin and laughs, Alan Kirk for frothy coffee, laughs, reams of paper and photocopying. The novelist Helen Stevenson for editing my awful punctuation, reminding me about gerunds and allowing peace with wine and beer chasers in Rousillon. R & R Cameron for laughing at my jokes and moral support. Kenny Gollan for laughs, car races and friendship; the Plockton and Badachro lots for reminding me there's no such thing as surreal, especially where blind rats or dead tups are concerned and Donald McA.Grant for confirming it, laughing and playing good tunes. S&L McLean for cash for new tyres and the contents of their fridge whenever they went on holiday, Charlie and Isobel McFarlane at Glenfinnan House Hotel for encouragement, credit, music, fun and petrol for the boat; John Whyte, Glenfinnan, for volcanic goat curry at 7.30am. The late Angus "The Gate" MacDonald of Moidart and Glenfinnan, for telling me everything he knew about Loch Shiel. The late Jean Campbell of Florida & Glenfinnan, for her encouragement and photographs, and the late Crispin Fisher, former Natural History Editor at Collins, who's faith in this book has kept me going through thick and thin.

To My Parents

Chapter 1

In the western Highlands of Scotland there is a long, narrow stretch of water that is called by men, Loch Shiel. It is an arm of the Atlantic, a great sea loch which runs north-east from the low, green Islands of Lorne in Big Firth, through a turbulent, steep sided narrows, and then, beneath high granite hills, continues mile upon clean sea mile, deep into the heart of the maritime Highlands.

Man has made his home there for many thousands of years. He has hunted on hillsides and high moors with weapons of bone and flint and then of iron. He has fished with traps of bent hazel and travelled in canoes and boats made also from bent hazel and covered and lined with the skins of beasts.

Long ago, mammoth, wolf and beaver lived on the land and boar and brown bear roamed through great forests of oak and ash. Deer drank from mountain streams and men came northward to hunt these beasts and know their ways: and those men were few, their settlements far apart.

The ice came, swallowing up the land and driving men and beasts into the south. The ice stripped hillsides and tore into the hearts of great mountains, gouging and shaping until at last, as long forgotten south winds returned, meltwater began to flow.

Slowly, as glaciers receded, meltwater carved for itself new courses and, as seasons emerged from perpetual winter, rivers ran in heavy flood during the months when nights were short and warm, carrying ice-ground silt from tall heights downwards, across low valleys and onward into the ocean. Green blade and bird and beast returned. And man came again to the Northlands and lived in caves and rough shelters from where he ventured out to eat roots and berries and the flesh of bird and beast and fish.

For thousands of years the land changed little save those parts used by men as they learned to reap and sow. On hillsides and in forests they harvested, killing deer and boar, and from Loch Shiel and all her feeder streams, throughout each summer they reaped a harvest of silver Salmon which they called Leaper, and its cousin, Tail Shaker, the Sea Trout.

Man shared his harvests with many creatures, knowing them all well. He understood three empires; the Land, the Sky and the Sea, and over all the first he saw himself as master. Above him in the Empire of The Sky ruled the creature he called Man Bird, or Black Eagle, which he esteemed for its courage, its powers of vision and soaring flight. Beneath him, in the depths of the sea he could not see but wondered at, man knew as ruler there the beast he thought half man, half animal, and called, the Seal. And the seal he revered not only for its grace in water, and, like the eagle, its skill in hunting, but also for its great knowledge of the past for which men thirsted, and called, The Ages.

Eagle and seal were of ancient lines. Their bloodlines were ancient before man had learned to stand straight or throw sticks at hungry wolves. There had been no first eagle, and no first seal, just as there had been no first, single man; for all had emerged only after the lessons of The Ages had been well learned. Seal, eagle and man, and all other living things had formed, forged on the anvil of time by fire and flood, to change, to adapt, to hide or to hunt. And in that ancient time all shared in matters of the earth and lived by the Ways and Laws of The Ages under a common rule of survival.

Off its southern shore lay most of the rocks and islets of Loch Shiel. Some were blanketed with long, wiry heather which blazed purple in late summer, and on almost all of the islands where heather grew there were tall pines with gnarled, spreading branches, and sometimes, straight, pale green larches which became bare in winter. The Island of Swords was the largest single islet and lay almost at the head,

or inland end of Loch Shiel, opposite The Village. Between
it and the stony shore was a wide, deep bay, known to men
and seals as Bay of Shelters, for even in the wildest winter
storms it showed little more than a ripple. In the bay, separated from Sword Island by a few seal's lengths of deep water
was a long, sloping slab of granite, almost hidden by the
island's short cliffs which overhung and sheltered it. Except
at the highest of tides there was space on the slab for half a
dozen seals and its long slope made access and escape easy.
It was the chosen Resting Rock of Rainha, the cow seal,
heavily pregnant with her unborn, fifth calf.

That rock had been used by seals since the ice had passed.
They had watched, generation upon generation, as men
settled on the hillside across the loch, living first in caves,
then huts made from rough boughs and branches, and then
in low, stone dwellings with turf roofs which are still in evidence today. They had watched, too, as men began to culti-
vate the soil and had learned to grow crops on the small,
fertile plain through which ran Rough River, fed from the
mountains above and running into the head of Loch Shiel,
separating the growing village from Bay of Shelters. Seldom
had man disturbed the seals here, but even so, they rarely
used the place to bring new pups into the world, preferring
another place, far from the activities of humankind.

★   ★   ★

Birthing Rock was treeless and low lying. Surrounded by
a thick bed of yellow kelp, it lay parallel to South Shore at
the central point of the loch and was about a hundred seal's
lengths from it, eight miles from both The Narrows and the
Village. Opposite Birthing Rock, a mile away on North
Shore was Bay of Otters, above which stood the tall, red
slabbed faces of Dun Mountain, the highest of Loch
Shielside and home to Talon the she eagle and her mate,
Chryso. Dun Mountain had two peaks, separated by a high,
toothed ridge which ran between them in a half circle over-
looking a deep, bowl shaped valley which had been reamed
out by force of ice ten thousand years before. This valley,

(called by men, a corrie,) joined the steep, lower slopes of
Dun Mountain by way of a narrow lip, or saddle, below
which the rocky debris of the glacier's passage had been scattered. Below those great, lichened boulders, oak and ash
formed a thick, richly carpeted forest which ran almost to the
shore and was home to all manner of birds and beasts. At its
edge, where the ground became too salt for other growth it
was heavy with bracken and bog myrtle. The forest ran the
full length of Loch Shiel, from The Narrows in the west, all
the way to The Village and far into the glen of Rough River
until the mountains became too high and bare for trees to
grow.

Of all the islets, Birthing Rock commanded the clearest
view in all directions, allowing a seal to look out from its low
summit to search for danger. Thousands of generations of
seals had been born there and many had perished as young
pups in sudden, summer storms, or under the beaks of Eye-
Peckers, grey crows and black backed gulls which stalked the
skies at pupping time in search of the weak or newborn
which could be killed as their mothers hunted or were driven
away by men.

Most of the offspring of the older cows survived, for
almost always they were born high on the rock, when the end
of a long summer day coincided with a high tide. Then, as
Eye-Peckers roosted, the falling tide gave a new pup a full
twelve hours before it would rise again high enough to force
the youngster into the sea. Nonetheless, each new seal came
into the world wearing a full, adult coat, allowing it to take
straight to the water, already insulated against the cold.

★   ★   ★

Rainha swam slowly towards Birthing Rock. She had been
in milk for several days and knew by The Ages that her time
was close. The new pup would depend on her alone and she
was watchful, sensing every change of tide and weather as
the moon waned and the summer solstice drew near.

It was a time of big tides and Rainha felt the tug of the ebb
as it gathered strength, eager for its seaward journey. As she

approached the rock she dived to the bottom which was sandy and bright before darkening in the shadow of the islet. She swam close to the bottom for a time, circling the rock almost completely before rolling on her back and rising slowly to the surface. She checked the height of the tide and peered around, looking to see if more of her Kind were there. Dusk was about to fall. The ebb had run barely an hour, but it was strong, too strong, she knew, and might flood back more strongly next morning and cover her intended Birthing Place, a few seal's lengths below the summit.

The seal was fitful; her pup had moved several times that day. Rainha had learned well and knew she must stay close to safety. Five years before she had seen her first pup, born on the eve of a summer gale, swept from a place, low on Birthing Rock by merciless pounding waves, wind driven through The Narrows from the Atlantic. The pup had drowned before being swept ashore on the rocks of Deer Grass Point and then devoured by Fox and Eye-pecker as Rainha had watched in vain. Only in such ways are the lessons of The Ages learned, and now, as the tide ebbed towards the red, western sky, the seal hauled high on Birthing Rock to rest and wait for the signs of The Ages to right themselves.

Across Loch Shiel, between the twin, shadow-blackened peaks of Dun Mountain, a dark shape soared slowly eastward towards his narrow, night ledge. As Chryso wheeled to land, the last light of dusk touched his wings and for a fleeting moment the eagle was cast in purest gold. For a full minute he stood, craning his neck to take a last view before night closed for a few hours the timeless book below him, and as he ruffed his feathers and made to hide his head beneath a wing, Rainha, far below on Birthing Rock, yawned deeply and waited for sleep.

Close to The Village in the wood called Owl Oaks, Strix wailed into the darkness and shook himself, preparing to hunt. His mate brooded three downy owlets in the warm hollow of an ancient tree, waiting as he searched the forest floor for voles and shrews with silent, moth-like flight, carrying them one by one back to the nest where they were welcomed by hungry, gaping beaks.

The night lived as Rainha slept. Many of her Kind hunted through the night, for by now a few Leapers and Tail Shakers had threaded their way from the ocean into Loch Shiel, seeking their birth streams. Foxes and badgers made their nightly rounds, mindful of hungry young mouths in dens and setts, and in every bog and bank and stream, living things worked to sustain themselves and their families throughout each moment of the short, Northland night.

★   ★   ★

The cow lay, waking and dozing in turn as the sun edged upwards, penciling the eastern ridges on a pale, dawning sky. From the lowest branches of rowan and oak, day birds stared down at dew laden heather, eager for food, and as the first hatch of insects rose from damp shores and the banks of streams, swallows and house martins appeared without call or warning to feast, swift and silent above the loch's margins. A ringing chorus of small birds began as the first swallows left, crop-full, to feed their young in mud-spit nests under the dusty eaves of barns and byres. The songs of thrush and blackbird vied with the notes of pipit and sandpiper, and the whole sound, the pure, ringing melody of The Ages rang, echoing through the valley of Loch Shiel before fading, quickly but almost imperceptibly, as hunger called again on wings to beat and seek the hard won riches of the land.

Shadows shortened soon after dawn broke, for the sun rises fast in a Northland summer and by seven the dew rises as steam from the backs of deer and seals. As Rainha woke fully and lifted her head to take stock of the new morning, the pup in her belly kicked violently. She heaved herself up and looked carefully at the tideline. It crept slowly upwards but she knew there was still a full hour of flood before the lull of slack water. The seal's mind was focussed solely on the respective heights of sun and tide. Bell clear, the day promised heat, and already, red deer and their spindly legged calves were climbing the ramparts of Dun Mountain to escape the torment of flies and baking temperatures of lower ground. By eight they would be on the tops, cooling themselves by small hill lochs which flecked the high plateau to the north, remaining there throughout the day until dusk took the heart from the sun and the land cooled and dampened, sweetening anew the grasses of the lower slopes.

As the tide reached a point half a seal's length below where Rainha lay it halted, then surged briefly again before slackening completely, now at full height. The seal watched, waiting patiently for the ebb to gather. Eventually it began to move, swirling slowly around Birthing Rock, tugging small pieces of flotsam, chips of wood and strands of broken bladder wrack from tiny crevices, tickling them until they broke free to join the tide on its journey. The water had risen to within only a few inches of the previous night's level, and now, Rainha knew that the distance between the heights of the high and low tides would continue to lessen until after the next full moon. Over the next two weeks, while tides were slack, most of the seal pups of Loch Shiel would be born. Then the main summer runs of Leaper and Tail Shaker would enter the loch seeking the Glen Scent of their birth streams, and shoals of mackerel and herring, rich in oils, would pass by on their southerly migration. All these would richen the milk of Rainha and her Kind, fattening their offspring according to the Ways of The Ages. Rainha felt her pup move again. She slid down the rock to the waters edge, and entering the cool of the loch, was filled with an ancient potency.

Chapter 2

Beyond The Narrows and the rich fishing grounds of Sallachan, and beyond the low, green Isles of Lorne where the grey Atlantic drives on to the high rock buttresses which stand in the way of the might of wind and sea, a small township is tucked into the coast. Below a steep semicircle of green hill lies a rock-flanked harbour, its small houses crushed tightly together and painted brightly to relieve the greyness of long winters. The town swells in summer as people arrive to sample peace far from their cities and enjoy the soft, slow pace among the colour and pure air of the Northlands. Pleasure boats, small yachts and cruisers visit the harbour, some arrived by sea from sheltered coastal towns and villages which dot the coast, and others, trailed there behind cars then launched from the small slipway.

As Rainha cooled herself in Loch Shiel, moving lazily between Birthing Rock and North Shore, one such boat was being wheeled towards that harbour twenty miles from where she swam. The boat was a small one, barely the length of three bull seals, but with a cabin and cheap, plywood bunks which doubled as seats and a table when turned over. On a bracket attached to the square stern hung a large engine which could push the boat along at a modest speed out of all proportion to the raucous noise it produced. On the left side of the stern and on each bow, the name, "Puffin," was emblazoned in scarlet letters against the white, polished hull.

The boat's owners, a man and woman in their early thirties, dressed in shorts and summer shirts, floated Puffin clumsily then tied the boat to the slipway before pushing the trailer back up the slope. They unloaded their car, paying scant attention to a fishing boat which waited patiently to tie up at the slipway and land its catch of pink, wriggling prawns. At length the car and trailer were parked and locked up. The noisy outboard was started, and with a casual wave to the fishermen on the waiting boat, Puffin was on the move, the man trying desperately to appear confident as he steered the boat through the narrow harbour mouth. They cleared the breakwater, and on entering Big Firth turned north towards the Islands of Lorne and the small cove where they planned to spend the first night of their holiday.

★   ★   ★

Throughout the morning Rainha rested at Birthing Rock, cooling herself in Loch Shiel whenever the heat became too much. It was only a few days before the solstice and by noon the sun was directly overhead, baking the rock as the tide fell and left it bare. The heat grew oppressive, and early in the afternoon the cow moved to North Shore, hauling out at the western end of Bay of Otters under the welcome shade of a small, damp cliff.

The ebbing tide exposed a long pebble beach which, from the slab of rock where Rainha lay, ran the full length of the bay to a grassy point about a hundred lengths away which marked its eastern end. Ringed plover and oystercatcher fed fussily among the stones close to the cow, knowing by The Ages that she would not harm them. An Eye-pecker, a grey backed crow landed near Rainha's tail and fixed her with a stare as though sensing the imminence of birth and the prospect of an easy meal. She allowed it to settle and relax a little, but then, turning her head with uncanny speed she lunged hard at it, missing only narrowly and sending the bird, flapping and cawing, out of sight.

Within an hour Rainha was completely dry. Her coat, ten months old since her last moult, had changed from the dark, slate colour it showed in the water, to a dull, creamy yellow, scattered over, except for her head and neck, with dark, thumbnail flecks which broke her outline as she lay ashore.

Just as on land she could confuse the vision of men, so too, in water she could swim at any depth virtually unseen by prey until close, perhaps too close, for it to escape. In August she would moult again, her old coat coming away in tufts as fresh, new fur grew in beneath. Now, bone dry and warm she scratched herself with her fore-flippers, supple joints allowing her to reach almost every part of her body where tiny sea-parasites sought last, life-giving droplets of salty water.

All through the afternoon she dozed peacefully, keeping one eye on the tide as it crept slowly upwards. Out of the shade the heat was still intense and the loch shimmered, making South Shore and Birthing Rock indistinguishable from each other from where the seal lay. The tide had been rising slowly for two hours and was already close to her slab when the seal decided to move. A V-shaped wave marked her passage across the loch to Birthing Rock, for the surface was like glass with not the slightest sign or promise of a breeze.

She hauled out, heaving herself up to a small niche below the summit of the islet. A roebuck, chestnut red in his summer coat, browsed among the willow scrub above the shore, and Rainha watched the beast, making sure it seemed settled and at ease, knowing then that no men roamed the shoreline. She shuffled round until comfortable and made sure that she had a full view of the loch before dozing again, waiting for evening.

★   ★   ★

Puffin had entered a small cove among the Islands of Lorne. It was a sheltered place where, in the past, before man raped the oceans and robbed the western seaboard of its harvests, many seals had hunted as the herring shoaled there in their hundreds of thousands. Now little used by fish or seals, it was a pretty anchorage, lying below grassy slopes and giving views of high, distant hills which turned pink as the sun fell. Once inside the bay the man reversed the engine, stopping Puffin dead in the water. The light, plastic boat rocked crazily as he moved forward to the foredeck and threw a light anchor over the bow, its chain rattling so loudly in the fairlead that he had to shout to his wife to tell her to reverse the engine and bring the cable tight. When satisfied the boat was safely anchored he stepped back along the side and jumped heavily into the cockpit where the two sat and ate, enjoying the peace and the view. When their meal was finished, its remnants, tins and plastic wrappers, were gathered up, tied into a bag then dropped casually into the clear, jade waters of the bay. Books and charts were laid out on the table: the talk was only of seals, how they might find them and get close to them.

That afternoon, chugging across Big Firth they had seen at least a dozen seals, but were unable to come closer than twenty lengths of a single one. Most had been basking on the surface enjoying the fine, calm weather or hunting lazily. Each time a seal was spotted the man shouted, and his wife, pink and naked, leaned perilously over the side with a camera as he drove the boat, its engine straining and pouring blue smoke, straight for the seal. On each occasion, his target, more annoyed than frightened, had dived into the depths of Big Firth to escape the dreadful noise, but the more they chased fruitlessly after the seals the more they became fascinated by them, and that night they lay in their bunks reading books which told them in words and pictures about the animals, though nothing at all about their need of peace.

* * *

Rainha had watched the sun dip behind Dun Mountain. Since mid-spring, nights had become short, lasting only a few hours, and even then, if the sky remained cloudless, never growing completely dark. Loch Shiel was still and shone like smoked glass in the long dusk as that time of evening came when no sound is heard: when creatures of the day are all retired and those of night not yet risen. The tide began to fall. The silence and stillness seemed almost to be a signal to the seal. She settled firmly in her niche, lying on her left side with her body braced as the new pup began its journey towards life.

Breathing steadily she concentrated on the task, stretching her body as the muscles of her belly moved the pup downwards. She shuddered as her birth waters flowed onto the rock, then pushed hard, writhing and twisting until at last, lying beside her tail, wet, shiny and covered with straggling patches of membrane, lay the new life she had carried for so many months.

The newborn pup lay still, its half open eyes flickering weakly. It appeared not to breathe, and as the cow looked down towards it she made low, murmuring sounds and pushed the frail youngster with a rear flipper. There was no response, but only after long seconds had passed did she nudge the pup again, staring at it and grunting loudly. But still it lay as though lifeless, and though she nudged once again the tiny creature wouldn't move. After a few more seconds she raised her tail flippers and brought them down hard over the youngster's back. Again she hit it, and again until at last it rolled downwards, squeaking and whimpering, to lie a few seal's lengths below its mother, now, clearly, very much alive.

The pup was mystified, confused; seeing and hearing nothing it knew, its understanding of consciousness only beginning to awake. It sneezed, blowing hard as its nostrils cleared of mucus and then, without warning as for the first time it took its mother's scent, bawled with almost the same sound as that of a newborn lamb. Rainha lay still, watching carefully as the pup discovered life. Unlike the mother of fox or badger she would not clean the pup or try to lick it dry, but would lie quite still, making low sounds and encouraging the tiny creature to move towards her. A new consciousness drove it to the smell that had first filled its nostrils. Whimpering, it discovered the use of its front limbs and gasped as it struggled to cover the short distance to its mother. As the pup grew closer, another, stronger scent urged it onwards to feel for the warmth of the cow's body and search blindly, pushing and bawling for the thick, yellow substance The Ages had told it to seek.

The quest grew more and more urgent as the pup neared Rainha's udder. Its movements became quicker and it reared again and again, driving its tiny face downwards each time against the cows belly until at last the secret was unlocked and Rondo, the new she-seal, drank her first, long draught. After only a few minutes she was exhausted and lay panting beside her mother. Rondo slept, and in the warm evening air her coat fluffed out as it dried, making her look plump and much heavier than her real weight of about that of a middle sized Leaper. She was the length of a man's hand and forearm, and quite dark, her face and neck covered in small, shiny wrinkles. The skin was loose, too, around the joints of her flippers which looked floppy and not really part of her body. Rainha sniffed softly at the pup but didn't waken it, and soon the mother cow herself drifted into sleep. As night sounds drifted in and out of the stillness, mother and daughter took their rest, and the tide, following its eternal course, ebbed through The Narrows to leave them high and dry, safe, at least till morning when the rising sun would herald the new dangers that arrived with every day.

★　★　★

Clear and cloudless, dawn crept into the world bringing no change to the peace and stillness of the loch. Rainha woke and looked up as two seals swam close, their wakes cutting the water to leave a sharp curling wave on each side of their necks. They both looked towards the rock and at the cow with her new pup, then cruised slowly up and down before hauling together into the thick tangle of weed at the tideline, grunting short, seal greetings.

Rondo woke, whimpering as after a few seconds she began to feel hunger. Seeking Rainha's udder she drank noisily, yellow, fatty milk running from each side of her mouth and down on to her drooping whiskers. When the udder had dried she tried hard to extract more, but the effort tired her and she collapsed panting onto her belly and fell asleep again almost immediately.

Across the loch, Dun Mountain was silvered by early light shining through a million dew drops which were held like crystal against the slope. Chryso peered from his night ledge,

stretched and shook dew from his feathers, watching the
droplets arc in a rainbow over the edge of the crag. Below
him, Talon stood on the edge of the great basket of a nest
gazing at her lone eaglet, asleep in the lined, central cup of
the eyrie. The young bird was more than half feathered, and
the white down it had already moulted was spread among
the bones of grouse and hare.

Talon looked out over the loch and saw on the steep slope
above Birthing Rock a small herd of hinds with young,
dappled calves grazing steadily upwards away from the heat
and flies. She knew Chryso would hunt before long, for
when the sun was high all wise creatures would hide from the
fierce heat reflected from so much rock and mountainside.
The eaglet must be fed by its parents for another two weeks
until fully fledged when they would begin to leave the young
bird hungry to encourage it to take wing. Once flying, their
interest would be renewed for perhaps a month or two until
it had mastered the rudiments of hunting and had begun to
fend for itself. Like the young seal, Rondo, Talon's eaglet
would spend its first winter alone, and finding food would be
no easier for eagle than for seal.

As warm air began to circulate around Dun Mountain,
Chryso felt the growing stream sweep upwards over the face
of his crag. Launching, he soared easily along the ridge using
the up-current to gain height, circling, searching the ground
as he rose in wide loops until the twin summits of Dun
Mountain were a thousand seal's lengths below him.
Wheeling, he glided across Loch Shiel, seeing clearly the
three adult seals and single pup on Birthing Rock. He passed
high above them on his way to the long ridge where earlier
he had watched deer grazing their way to the tops.

Perhaps some luckless animal, lame or sickly, or caught in
a tight gully and unable to rejoin its mother, would feed him
and his eaglet that day, but the beasts had already gone high
over the ridge onto the vast plateau beyond, where there was
so little cover for him that hunting down even the most sickly
calf would waste too much energy. Gathering his wings he
lost height quickly and soared low along the lower slopes,
quartering the ground and using contours and shadows to

hide his progress. Finding nothing he rose in a thermal which carried him effortlessly back above the ridge from where he could retrace his flight from Dun Mountain with the least amount of work.

⋆   ⋆   ⋆

Rainha, alert beside her sleeping pup, watched the small, black speck pass above but showed no alarm, for only once in her life had she seen an eagle attack a young seal, and knew by The Ages that this bird, Chryso, would not approach them. She lost sight of him as he flew north- west and crossed North Shore, still high, but now with his eyes fixed firmly on where he had seen the slightest movement below the lip of Dun Mountain Corrie. A mountain hare, his summer coat pale blue to blend with the heather, had crossed a patch of green woodrush. Chryso's peerless vision had picked him out, and now, gathering speed, the eagle plummeted on half-closed wings towards a high cliff which stood above the unsuspecting beast. With the sun behind him he cartwheeled in the sky, and then, wings clenched, dropped like a lazy, hanging cannonball out of the dazzling glare.

The hare saw him only as the eagle threw out his wings to brake before the strike, his golden tail fanned out ready to steer should the hare jink sideways. Unable to reach cover, as Chryso stooped the hare sprang like a cricket in a desperate attempt to escape by jumping clean over the eagle. But Chryso was old and many skilled; both legs were coiled in readiness and as his quarry leapt he stretched with lightning speed, one talon fastening to the hare's head, crushing its skull, the other clasping its back. They fell the final length to the ground in a bundle, the hare already dead. The eaglet would eat today.

The bird tore at the hare with wings spread over it like a mantle. He paused, looking around as though deciding whether to eat or not and then, grasping the beast in one foot, launched from the slope and beat upwards, carrying the meal to a safer place. He split the beast, taking the larger part directly to Talon at the eyrie before returning to gorge himself on what remained.

As winter had turned to earliest spring, Talon had laid two eggs and hatched both of them. Since then, although Chryso had supplied all their food it had fallen only to Talon to tear off small strips of meat from what had been caught and hold them out to her ever hungry eaglets. At first they were fed only meat, progressing after a week or so to both meat and fur, then, bone, meat and fur together. She had not fed her eaglets evenly, but gave most to whichever had been stronger and more aggressive in pushing to the front. The female eaglet, even though she had hatched four days later than her brother, had from birth been larger and stronger, and so had grabbed the greater share of food, bullying the male mercilessly as he grew weaker and weaker, until she managed to eject him from the eyrie to fall to his death on the corrie floor.

For about a week now, Talon had no longer torn up food for the remaining eaglet, for she had grown strong and learned to grab and tear for herself without the mother bird's assistance. As Chryso dropped the hare on the edge of the eyrie, Talon had almost been knocked over as her offspring made a vicious, hungry dive, grabbing the beast then bouncing back to the far side of the great basket, half feathered wings spread in defiance and calling;...Cilree...Cilree... Cilree.

Talon flew to the ledge where Chryso devoured his quarry. As she landed he looked at her and moved aside to let her eat: but hunger was not with her and she settled a wing's breadth from him to preen herself then take some rest. From the ledge the birds could see the full length of Loch Shiel, and to the west, beyond The Narrows, the specks which shimmered in Big Firth were the Islands of Lorne, where the crew of Puffin had just stirred from salty, seal filled dreams.

Chapter 3

They woke to a morning they could not quite believe. In the cove, pale, jade coloured water shone like a mirror. High, distant mountains stood, streaked and patterned, their topmost ridges etched onto the washed blue of a sky which seemed to stretch cloudlessly to the very edge of the universe. The air was fresh and salt clean and dew steam rose from lush, green grass and bracken that fringed the bay. Sitting quietly, drinking coffee in the small cockpit of the boat away from sight or sound of other folk and with only the music of small birds drifting from the island, they felt that strange uncanny peace so seldom found in their other world, where all is moulded by the hand of man.

Almost reluctantly they began to plan the day. They would have liked to stay there, to swim in the cove perhaps and explore the small isle which all but surrounded their anchorage, but the seals drew them. A course was laid off on the chart which would bring them to The Narrows by about midday. The anchor was brought aboard and stowed away, and as the morning lengthened, Puffin entered Big Firth and turned to the north-east.

The boat chugged along, its crew transfixed by endless, long views, until about the time when the sun reached full height, they reached the fishing grounds of Sallachan. Seals appeared here and there, but Puffin could make no headway for the ebb now boiled in full force through The Narrows into Big Firth and they could not attempt to follow a beast in case they were swept back. They struggled on, worried now by the strength of the tide and looking for a refuge until it slackened. Eventually, after heading towards the north side of the Firth, they were carried into a long bay out of the main stream where their anchor held in thick mud. Relieved, still frightened by what they had seen of the water's power they settled to wait, content to scour loch and hillside with giant binoculars, discussing everything they saw.

They had planned to spend that night at a small group of rocky islets a few miles into Loch Shiel from The Narrows which, with the flood behind them, were only about forty minutes from where Puffin now lay at anchor. The high hills and the waters of the loch beckoned as they looked at the chart, and now, with time to spare, they studied it more closely than before. Five miles beyond their planned destination they saw a small outcrop close to South Shore named on the chart, Sgeir nan Roinn. Translated from the language of the Gael, this means, The Rock of The Seals: and to those creatures, it is their Birthing Rock.

★   ★   ★

After her early feed Rondo had slept again for a few hours and then, at about seven, wakened to her first full day on the planet. Her vision, like her limbs, needed time to grow strong, and for a few days all but the closest things would seem blurred and strange. Dry but for a few remaining drops of dew, the pup looked tiny beside her mother and was a uniform, shiny slate grey, in contrast to Rainha's creamy off-white. The wrinkles on her face bunched tightly when she yawned or turned to squeak to her mother. Her neck was thin, still lacking the muscle and blubber which would form beneath her skin with the help of Rainha's milk. For the next few weeks, though not strong, the pup would not be completely helpless, for The Ages had given her the ability to swim from birth; even to be born in the water. Her first attempts would be clumsy and she would not be able to endure rough weather or any long period in the water without feeding often to replace the heat and energy she would lose, so for the first three or four days Rainha would stay very close, reassuring and guiding Rondo, ever vigilant for Eye-Peckers and man.

The pup fed again then lazed in the shade of Rainha's bulk, squeaking occasionally to attract a motherly grunt or nuzzle. As the morning wore on and grew hot, the bottle-green water rose to within a few lengths of the seals, and Rondo, suspicious at her first sight of what would be the most important thing in her life, peered haltingly, pulling her head back sharply when the water swirled, like a young dog encountering its first, unyielding cat. Rainha was relaxed, for no Eye-Peckers had flown near them and neither had she seen boats or other signs of man. She felt the heat on her back and knew that young Rondo would have to be cooled when the sun stood high, for that sun could be as quick to injure or kill as extreme cold, and must be treated with respect.

The youngster watched closely as strands of bladder wrack and old leaves floated past only a seal's length from her. As the tide slackened and sat lazily at full height, the pup lost some of her nervousness and craned outwards to sniff the water, searching dimly with moist, black eyes for some clue as to what it was or why it was there. Ever more fascinated and perhaps recognising some strange sense or smell, she leaned further and further across the short distance to the waters edge, until, lying parallel to the tideline she over-reached and rolled, squealing, down the short, steep slope into the cold loch. Bawling like a lamb she wallowed help-lessly, thrashing the water with all four flippers at the edge of Birthing Rock. Rainha grunted then slid to the waters edge. Rondo came to her, spluttering as she tried to regain the safety of the rock, but the cow held her, pushing the pup back into the shallows with her nose each time Rondo tried to clamber out, until soon she grew accustomed to feeling the water around her and lay quietly, still puzzled but no longer frightened. The cow allowed the pup to settle a while, then moved slowly into the loch. Rondo stayed where she was, whistling and blowing as she saw her mother move away. Rainha stopped, almost completely submerged and facing out into the loch, ignoring the pup as it vented its disapproval, but doing nothing to encourage it to move.

Very slowly, Rondo moved forward, surprised at how easy

it was as more and more of her small body became immersed. Without thinking she began to move her front and rear limbs, holding her head as high as she could out of the water. She looked around quizzically, and feeling her mother move, began to follow until they were a dozen lengths from Birthing Rock. Rondo was afloat. She was not frightened, for Rainha was beside her and she swam easily, finding a freedom she had not experienced on land. Her rear limbs pushed her along and she found herself steering by twisting her body and using her front flippers: and it was cool, more comfortable there in the loch than on the hot rock. Her head was still held high and she spluttered a little as Rainha turned and she was forced to make an extra effort to keep up. Now, the two seals faced Birthing Rock, and Rainha stopped and lay still in the water so young Rondo could take her first view of her birthplace from the seaward side. The pup looked hard, trying to take everything in, almost as though she realised the importance of these moments. She sniffed the air and at the mingling smells of salt sea, kelp and wrack, among which, the mother smell of Rainha told her she was safe.

The cow began to play gently with her pup, pushing lightly and rolling her from side to side, making the youngster squeak with apprehension. As the young seal began to lose some of her nervousness, Rainha swam away a little so the pup was forced to follow, which she did without fear, now enjoying each new sensation more and more. Then, just as she became used to following her mother, Rainha dived, swimming down vertically until she was about three or four seal's lengths below, waiting for Rondo to follow.

The pup was confused again: she didn't understand where her mother had gone and twisted frantically from side to side, snorting and grunting in fright as she looked for Rainha. She took a first, irresolute look below the surface, but in the frightening second or so she kept her head under she saw nothing. But something told her to try again, and this time she found it easier; much easier, certainly, than trying to hold her head high out of the water above the ripples. She pushed slowly with her rear limbs, moving ahead by a few lengths, now with her head beneath the surface. Fear of losing Rainha was being replaced by fascination with what she had begun to see, and as her eyes began to focus for the first time under water, she saw just below her the outline of a dark shape drifting across her field of vision. She pulled back, lifting her head, blowing and drawing breath rapidly, more in anticipation of her next glance beneath the loch than in fear or fright. She held her head straight out now, almost craning to catch a closer look; but the shadow had gone, it was nowhere to be seen.

Rainha watched as the pup drew breath then pushed her head below the ripple once again. The cow let herself sink slowly to the bottom, keeping her eyes firmly fixed on Rondo and swimming a short distance until no longer directly below the youngster. She couldn't tell if she was able to see her or not, but still, didn't attempt to move closer. Instead, she circled slowly upwards heading for a point just below the surface and two or three lengths behind the pup's tail. She rolled swiftly creating turbulence and watching carefully as the pup felt the swirl and turned, to see again the shadow she had lost a few moments ago. The young seal moved haltingly towards the shape, but already Rainha was moving downwards, not vertically this time, but in a shallow, slow dive so the pup could follow her progress.

Rondo was baffled and pushed her head further and further under the water. She felt herself tipping forward and moved her front flippers to recover, but instead of coming level, found herself moving downwards. Without thinking she body-rolled, looking up as she passed through one-hundred and eighty degrees. She was now two seal's lengths below the surface, hanging motionless and baffled. She had seen nothing above her and now, her young, misty eyes scoured the water below. Something moved, not directly beneath her but down to her left; it was hardly discernible, – a flicker, but she went after it almost without thinking, hardly noticing that she was totally immersed for the very first time, moving easily into a strange, new world.

The tide had begun to ebb and she found herself steering to counter the small current by pushing slowly ahead with her rear flippers. Below, she saw for the first time the world that was to be her home, playground and larder. The water was clear and her eyes were becoming used to changing focus as they fixed on objects at different distances away. The shadow she tried to follow was moving slowly in a wide circle below. When she lost sight of it she stopped and hung motionless to search again, but she couldn't seem to get any closer and her attention was being taken by other, new things which kept appearing almost everywhere she looked. A small Tail Shaker, perhaps frightened by the cow nearby, shot past the pup heading for the rocky cover of North Shore. Rondo felt the urge to follow, but the fish was gone in moments and she lost interest quickly.

The shape had gone now. No matter where she looked she could not find it again. Rondo was alone, the new world she had explored with such growing interest a few minutes ago was quickly losing fascination and growing dark and frightening. She drifted slowly in the current, looking this way and that, hoping for some small sign of Rainha that she could recognise as apprehension and now, hunger, grew in her belly. All comfort was gone: all interest in her new surroundings and joy of discovery had disappeared and she was miserable and frightened. Then, just as she began to panic, something she couldn't see touched her and she shot to the surface in a welter of bubbles, bawling loudly in fright. There, only a seal's length away, was Rainha.

She had sneaked up behind the pup, nipping one of Rondo's tail flippers gently before swerving away and diving to the bottom. The pup, already almost rigid with fright at being lost, reacted violently, powering to the surface to draw breath and make her escape. Panic turned to happiness and the bawling grew louder, then, flapping noisily through the water, she was safe at Rainha's side and settled down, nuzzling the cows face and greeting her thankfully in the tongue of their Kind.

The cow sensed the pup's tiredness and moved slowly towards Birthing Rock, allowing Rondo to slide onto her back and be carried. She touched bottom close to the rock and began to haul out, rolling slightly to tell Rondo it was time to get off. But the pup held fast, and only as Rainha hauled jerkily up the slope, no longer able to keep hold of her mother she tumbled onto the hard rock, squeaking in annoyance. She followed the cow almost to the top of the islet, and even as Rainha shuffled round to face the open loch, Rondo was already at the udder, drinking thirstily.

A young cow, ready to pup, had hauled up onto an open, flat part of Birthing Rock as they had played in the loch. Rainha heard the quickness of breath as the beast strained to deliver and looked round anxiously, for the inexperience of the young animal in giving birth in such an obvious part of the Rock might bring Eye-Peckers in droves, creating grave danger for Rondo. The pup was born and within a few minutes was squeaking as it searched the cow for milk.

Soon, as both pups slept, gulls and crows began to arrive as though drawn by some silent, primeval message to float in the sky above Birthing Rock. At first they circled with no apparent aim or destination, only the occasional bird breaking ranks with the wider ring and slanting casually inwards towards the islet for a closer look. Before the birth of the young cow's pup, not a single bird had been in sight. Now, as the circle tightened, there was cawing of grey crows and screeching of black-backed gulls, – muted at first, but rising, always rising as they closed the rock, the red-ringed, yellow eyes of gulls and cruel, black eyes of the crows fixed on Rondo and the newborn pup, then on the mother cows, gauging distances and speeds, judging strategy and tactics, the effort required and the possibility of success: and all the time looking everywhere around them, everywhere there may be risk or danger to an Eye-pecker, all in the Way of The Ages.

Soon they were above the seals, now awake and looking upwards to the great swirling of birds. Lower they flew, ever lower until the gulls skimmed the loch and crows flapped weakly, trying to hover over the rock. Some black-backs landed on the water and drifted slowly towards the seals, and a few crows alighted on the western end of Birthing Rock from where they could hop closer to the new pup's after-birth, already drying quickly and beginning to stink, only a seal's length from the tail of the younger cow.

Rainha grunted in a low tone to Rondo, letting her know in the tongue of seals that there was danger and she must stay near. The pup of the younger animal was not so close to its mother, but the cow, although disquieted by the Eye-Peckers, had done nothing yet to bring it closer to her. A few gulls had now landed on the islet among the crows, though most sat floating comfortably on the loch, waiting for those on the rock to begin the ancient rite before flapping in, shrieking in eagerness for the feast. Rondo looked round nervously and huddled closer to her mother, sensing danger from the birds but not knowing in what form it might come. Rainha knew they would have to take to the water to escape the Eye-Peckers, but had, if possible, to give her pup sufficient time to recover from their swim and, too, for the feed she had taken to work and replace Rondo's lost energy. But the birds grew ever closer, hopping insolently right up to the straggle of dull, red afterbirth, testing the young cow's reaction to their incursion, steadily invading the seals' space.

A grey crow hopped up to the afterbirth and made as if to drag it out of reach of the cow. Two or three times it moved in like that, and when the bird knew that the cow could not or would not attack, it grabbed the stringy remains in its beak and half hopped, half flew to the waters edge where all its cousins descended to fight for a share in the prize. The larger gulls won the day, bullying the crows out of the way to be left only with scraps. For a while, until the afterbirth was finished there was an uneasy calm, but already, crows and gulls were taking up position for the main assault.

Rainha's head was up and she was ready to move into the water with Rondo at her side. But she waited, for the bulk of Eye-Peckers had begun to close in on the pup of the younger cow and she knew she must wait until the birds were distracted in some way. Gull and crow moved, one by one, into a tight ring around the young cow and her pup. They began the work of The Ages, two or three taking the cow's attention by hopping in and out of her range as others pecked lightly at the pups tail, never staying close for more than a few seconds, perhaps realising the youth and inexperience of the youngster's mother. For a while she was patient, more interested in staying close to her pup than in spending energy lunging at birds, but the attack intensified and blows rained on the pup with increasing frequency and force, tiring the tiny beast as it twisted and turned, snapping in futile attempts to defend itself. Without warning the cow's patience snapped. Rearing, she turned, pushing her pup aside as she slashed with teeth and flippers at the gathering of birds, almost leaping from the rock as she struck like a snake at the breast of a gull which was trying desperately to lift from the ground under a welter of frightened wings. She grasped the bird in her teeth, crushing flesh and bone with the power of her jaws, shaking it in awesome, single minded rage and throwing the limp bundle into the air in high, wingless flight, arcing over the slope to the edge of Birthing Rock, dying now, the scarlet of its blood a warning to all its Kind.

Small, downy breast feathers hung in the air as the dead bird drifted seawards under the cacophony of fleeing predators. The young cow began to settle, blowing hard through her nose as anger turned to relief, and the tiny, wrinkled pup, badly shaken but undamaged, nuzzled her neck, squeaking softly.

The Eye-Peckers disappeared into the brilliant blue above The Narrows and were soon lost in the sun's dazzle. Wherever they went there would be food for them: on fell or foreshore they would chance on something to fill their crops, but still, would fly this way again before dusk in case some mishap should befall either pup before the day's end. The grey crows separated over Black Rocks, peeling away to land and view the wide foreshore from tall pines. The gulls flew onwards, and as they cleared the gateway of The Narrows, crossed the path of a small, white boat, inbound for Loch Shiel.

Chapter 4

Throughout the long, hot afternoon a number of seals gathered at Birthing Rock and all spoke in the tongue of their Kind, greeting and warning in grunts and murmurings as they came and went. Eventually about twenty seals lounged on the rock and others swam or hunted lazily nearby. Many were tied by blood and all were known to each other according to the Ways and Messages of The Ages as it had been since the days of The Seal Fathers.

Among the group, minor arguments took place from time to time, most of which concerned basking space on the rock. Sometimes bulls fought over a mate, sustaining bloody injuries, and very occasionally two animals would become deadly enemies, their feud lasting throughout their lives until one died naturally or was killed, or both grew too old and lazy to bother with fighting. But feuds resulting in death were rare, for above all, the seals loved peace to hunt or bask as they pleased and take what was necessary to sustain life as The Ages had decreed. All had their place there, young and old, bull and cow, determined not by birth but by deed and the ability of each to survive.

Birthing Rock baked under the sun and the seals cooled themselves from time to time, swimming and hunting half seriously for the small flatfish, dabs and sole which abounded in the sand and mud of the loch bottom close to the islet. Rainha sat tight among the gathered seals, leaving only once as a cousin hauled out close by, near enough to pass as Rondo's mother should the Eye-Peckers return. She cooled herself within sight of the sleeping pup and returned only when Rondo woke and bawled anxiously for mother scent and milk. By early evening a breeze began to lift, and once more, Rondo was taken to continue her discovery of the world beneath the sea.

★   ★   ★

Six miles from Birthing Rock the first draughts of breeze were welcomed by Puffin's crew. They had spent a few hot hours exploring the Black Rocks, picnicking before searching for nests and other signs of wildlife. They spoke in loud voices and crashed about so noisily that everything on the islets had either hidden or flown away, so after pulling up some heather and small shrubs to take home they stumbled back over rocks and tussocks to the short stretch of sand where Puffin was pulled up. Backing out slowly, they photographed the pines and larches, circling the rocks a few times before heading into the loch and turning north-east.

They had decided it would be too dangerous to anchor for the night at Black Rocks, for there were too many reefs and boulders scattered around, so they studied the chart again. The only place in the loch appeared to be at Bay of Shelters, but it was close to the houses and people they were on holiday to avoid and with no wish for company, their eyes fell once again to Sgeir nan Roinn, The Rock of The Seals.

Despite being little more than a speck on the chart and having a name the two could not pronounce, let alone translate, they thought they might anchor safely between the islet and the land. They steered the boat closer to South Shore so they would not miss the place. Within ten minutes they had it in sight and the man, seeing a small dark shape in the loch heading towards the rock, shouted excitedly to his wife. They followed the seal's progress as it closed Birthing Rock and swam close to its western end without hauling out.

Through binoculars he saw a movement high on the rock followed quickly by a splash at the waterside as a nervous young bull took refuge in the loch. Puffin's bow was pointed straight at Birthing Rock and the seals there watched anxiously as the boat came ever closer. A few more followed the young bull into the loch, but most watched silently to see what would happen next, for fishing boats and yachts often circled the islet and as long as they posed no clear threat and weapons were not raised or loud noises made the older seals tended to sit tight, though ready to streak into the water at once should they sense danger.

The woman, too, was watching Birthing Rock, and as her eyes adjusted to the slight contrast between stone and animal, she saw them all. She shouted, "seals – lots of seals!" Her voice pierced the stillness. The seals heard it, saw her white arms waving and the flash of sun on glass, and the water boiled as they raced for the deeps. Only two remained. High on Birthing Rock, both motherless, lay Rondo and the pup of the young cow.

The little plastic boat edged to within a few seal's lengths of the rock. Inexperienced and worried about damaging his precious craft, the man backed it away so he could ascertain the depth more clearly. The two pups had lain silently as their mothers cruised close to the islet, fearful of hauling out in case the intruders meant them harm. Puffin was now about twenty seal's lengths from Birthing Rock, and though her crew had not yet seen the two pups, the younger had grown fretful and squeaked and whistled for its mother. The sun's glare and the pups' natural camouflage had, until now, kept them hidden, but the cries of the younger animal made the man look harder, using his big, unwieldy binoculars to search for the source of the noise.

When he saw them lying below the summit he shouted to his wife. They rushed to anchor the boat which, after it was moored, lay only fifteen seal's lengths from the rock. Very soon the new flood tide swept them back on the long anchor chain so Puffin's stern settled only a short distance from the western end of the islet, close to the two pups and adding to the crew's excitement as they rushed around noisily with cameras and binoculars, unaware that the cries they heard were those of desperate fear.

Rainha and the young cow were powerless while the crew of Puffin remained active. They dared not risk hauling out, for they may be killed or injured by the intruders and, according to The Ages, at such a time they must risk the lives of their pups before their own so that if any harm were done it would not be to themselves and they could mate again to bring other pups into the world to replace those that might have perished.

The man and his wife jabbered excitedly, moving around in the boat, changing lenses and throwing lumps of bread into the water, trying to attract the two seals which had stayed close to the rock. They couldn't understand why they would come no closer and take the food they offered, failing totally to connect them with the pups which lay squeaking nearby and slowly exhausting themselves. The woman thought the sounds they made were sweet and, when she and the man had calmed down a little, they sat in the cockpit watching until the light faded and the pup's cries grew ever weaker. Only when they could no longer make out the shapes of the young animals against Birthing Rock and it grew cool and damp, did their thoughts turn to sleep.

*   *   *

The last light on the boat had been out for half an hour before Rainha and the younger cow edged slowly towards the rock. Rainha swam watchfully on the surface, stopping every few lengths to gaze suspiciously at Puffin which, now that the tide had topped out and begun to ebb strongly, had swung towards The Narrows in the seaward flow and lay a good thirty seal's lengths from Birthing Rock. An approach was now much safer and, closely followed by the younger seal Rainha dived, surfacing again only when she gained the rock. Rondo caught the mother scent as the cow slid ashore and whistled anxiously for a few seconds until Rainha had come to her and she could nuzzle and be reassured. Within a few minutes all that could be heard on the rock were the greedy sounds of both pups suckling, and both soon felt the warmth of milk fill them with new strength.

Both youngsters, exhausted and without food for longer than was safe, filled their bellies and then, the evening's unhappy memories already fading, fell quickly into deep, untroubled sleep. Stress and hunger had weakened them, but as long as they were disturbed no further and not kept from their mothers, no lasting harm would be done. But in a few more hours, when daylight crept across the land towards them, danger would abound, for late that evening, Eye-Peckers, flying homeward, had marked well the two new pups lying on Birthing Rock.

*   *   *

Young Rondo woke and looked mistily about her. Yawning, she stretched, fanning out her infant flippers. She was hungry, and squeaked, heaving herself the short distance to where her mother lay and suckled. Rainha woke and looked up, gazing suspiciously at Puffin from which, as yet, there was no sound. The sounds of night, too, had gone, and the cow could see deer close to the mainland shore, feeding hurriedly on sweet, damp grasses before the sun rose and its fire drove them upward again in search of a cool breeze and freedom from the flies that would soon begin to plague them. Looking round, Rainha saw the younger cow above her with the dark, wrinkled pup, its mouth stained yellow where the remains of its last feed had dried. Both cows scanned the loch as daylight grew and sounds of dawn began. It was after daybreak, and as the tide turned and the ocean flooded back towards the land, Puffin swung slowly on her chain to place her flat stern, once again, only a few seal's lengths from Birthing Rock.

The two seals watched closely as the boat settled. The younger cow grunted in alarm, but nothing stirred aboard the craft and apart from the sounds of birds and the splashing of a few Leapers agitated by the flood tide as it swirled in the channel between Birthing Rock and South Shore, the loch was calm and peaceful. But for the presence of Puffin, the cows would have been waterborne on hearing Leapers, challenging by stealth, sliding close to the bottom, waiting for the salmon to settle and drift down out of the light towards them. But today's dawn was too uncertain, and the cows, wisely, stayed with their pups, for even as the sounds of birds and Leapers drifted across Loch Shiel, the first Eye-

Peckers were already lifting from branch and bough to fly seaward. Birthing Rock was on their path.

Two more seals arrived, a bull and a two year old cow. They eyed Puffin suspiciously but nonetheless, flopped onto the rock and hauled up below Rainha and her dozing pup, making greetings in the tongue of seals as they settled and began to clean and preen themselves. The dawn remained cool and the hillside below Dun Mountain had become silvered as the sun crept upwards and caught dewdrops in every ray. The new arrivals continued preening, scratching lazily at their coats and wiping long, wiry whiskers with each flipper. A small shadow crossed the rock, and as it passed the two mother cows looked up in alarm. It was a grey crow, a single bird which flew straight on towards The Narrows before turning and circling high in the air, drifting back slowly to the watching seals. Then, as the bird was above them, there came a cry which put fear into the hearts of the mother cows. It was the shrieking of black backed gulls: the death cry of the great Eye-pecker.

They came towards Birthing Rock out of the east, their consort of a dozen grey crows flying a little ahead and below them. The gulls landed on South Shore across the channel from Birthing Rock, and the crows, vanguard of this malevolent company, circled soundlessly above the seals and made ready to alight. The two cows shuffled closer to their pups, hissing now, their eyes rolling in menace. A crow landed by the summit and cawed its evil greeting to the seals, his dark beak thrust forward aggressively. Another landed, and another, until after a few minutes they were spread, all cawing and hopping, along the summit of the rock.

As the last crow landed the gulls took to the air and screamed their way across the channel, landing in the water close to the islet from where they might watch the crows begin their deadly work. The pups were bewildered and frightened; their mothers watched, heads up, looking round sharply as each bird moved to play its part. It was a game forged on the anvil of The Ages, a long, tactile battle of nerves as Eye-Peckers watched for weakness or inattention and worked together to unnerve with all the time in the world to complete their task. As on the previous day they might yet be put to flight, but they would always return again, taking every chance The Ages offered to fill their crops with young seal meat. They worked noisily along the ridge, hopping, cawing, coming closer and closer with every minute.

Suddenly they rose, crying loudly, for on the small, white boat a door had opened, swinging round on its cheap hinges to crack like a rifle shot against the plastic bulkhead which supported it. As the man clambered into the cockpit, four adult seals hit the water in a single movement. He stood at the side of the boat holding the cabin top as he emptied his bladder into the glassy loch. He peered sleepily towards the rock from where he had heard the splash as the seals fled, and now heard crows and gulls cawing and screaming above him, but the low sun glared, blinding him to all but a blur of shapes. Finishing his ablution, he leaned into the cabin for a box of matches and seated himself on a side bench to light the small, gas stove. As the kettle boiled he smoked a cigarette, listening to the raucous cries of the Eye-Peckers as they circled, ever lower, joyful now, expectant, knowing that the cows had left their pups. Three birds landed together and the younger beast snarled bravely as one of them sidled towards its wrinkled face. Rainha watched in frustration from the water as the crows gathered, thrashing her tail and head in a vain attempt to frighten the birds. The man still sat in the cockpit, and neither cow would dare risk moving closer while he remained there. The younger pup was surrounded now and bawled in fright as the Eye-Peckers tightened their ranks, hopping closer, bouncing back only when the youngster snapped at them, but closing; closing in all the while.

Spitting, the younger pup turned rapidly as a crow struck at the soft skin of its rear flippers then hopped quickly back out of reach. Another pecked lightly at the pup's neck before it could turn, then yet another attacked its rear limbs. One by one they harried the youngster, pecking lightly, not breaking the skin but tiring and weakening the animal as it tried bravely to fight them off. Rainha and the young cow watched helplessly as the crows worked. The Black Backed gulls, now closer to the shore than the mother seals dared venture, screamed encouragement to the crows. The cows barked and whistled at their young, trying desperately to get them into the water, but the younger beast was too busy, too pre-occupied in trying to fight off the crows to pay attention, and both pups had eyes and ears for nothing but the battle lines forming around them.

★   ★   ★

The man watched from the cockpit then stood, shading his eyes with a hand against the glare as he tried to make out the cause of the commotion, even now, not connecting the two seals he could see so close to the boat with the noise on Birthing Rock. The younger cow, less cautious than Rainha, thrashed the water, spinning and beating her flippers on the surface, barking to her pup which squealed fearfully in acknowledgement. Its head rolled violently from side to side, teeth flashing in defiance as it tried to avoid the birds, all cawing or screeching joyfully, sensing the pup was weaken-ing until, as the young beast threw its head back in a final, wild snarl, it overbalanced and rolled down the slope to lie breathless and shaking beside an equally fearful Rondo.

For a few moments the crows were in disarray, but soon gathered again, still concentrating on the younger, already weakened pup, which shook in terror as they approached. Then, hearing its mother's call, the youngster looked down and saw a cow at the waters edge, driven there in despera-tion despite the man's presence. Ignoring the Eye-Peckers the pup made for its mother, finding new strength as it took her scent and splashing thankfully into the loch just as the man realised what was happening and began to beat vio-lently on the side of the boat to scare off the mass of birds, so that as the exhausted pup was shepherded from the island by its mother, the sky above Rondo grew dark with rising Eye-Peckers.

Gradually the air cleared as the birds circled higher and higher above the rock. The man disappeared into the cabin to speak to his wife who was now awake and asking anxiously

about the noise and what had been happening. He sat in the doorway facing inwards, explaining. Silently, the gulls and crows ringed ever lower and began, once again, to settle.

Rondo heard the wingbeats above, but the shock of events together with her undeveloped vision made sure she saw no more than blurred shapes. The crows dropped again onto Birthing Rock, more slowly this time, and silently, much more cautious of the boat and its crew, their death cries muted but their purpose still unchanged. Rainha watched from twenty seal's lengths, her fear growing afresh as the birds gathered in a wide circle around her pup. She murmured and blew hard through her nose but Rondo heard nothing, for the blurred shapes had become real and, once again, blood and adrenalin coursed through her as the birds hopped grotesquely, closing on her tiny, wrinkled form. A gull landed half a seal's length away and glared at Rondo through red-ringed, yellow eyes. Its beak, too, was yellow, brilliant against the dull black of its feathered back; and above the deadly, tearing tip was a stripe of purest crimson, marking it as the weapon of a killer; an executioner of the young or weak; appointed by The Ages to the task.

The black-back watched as the crows began to work. More gulls landed; three or four, and stood with necks stretched forward and open beaks, their eyes bright, glinting in stark contrast to the dullness of the crows they encouraged. Rondo spat as the first Eye-pecker risked her small, sharp teeth, then whistled loudly as she felt the touch of a beak low down on her back. She lay flat on her belly with her teeth and bright pink gums bared as she faced the birds. A gull weaved slowly just above her and she slashed at it, only to feel a rain of blows on her back as the crows now took their chance. Rondo turned, shivering with fear and fright and every undeveloped muscle tensed as she fought valiantly against the onslaught, energy already flooding from her. She tried to rear up but was too weak, too undeveloped to obey The Ages' Message, and even as she snarled bravely, a hammer blow to the base of her skull flattened her on to the hard rock, filling every part of her with searing, numbing pain. Breathless, she felt the skin tear as the executioner

struck a second time. Summoning every ounce of her remaining strength she twisted violently to attack the black back,
but violence, grim and purposeful, descended on her like a
shroud. The gull had aimed a blow at Rondo's face, and
even as she raised her head to slash at the bird its cruel beak
landed with terrifying power to pierce the seal's left eye. She
gasped in pain, expelling every drop of breath, but again the
gull struck, tearing flesh around the wound as the seal now
lay flat with her limbs outstretched, her body limp and
almost as though already dead, unable to do anything as the
final rain of blows drove into her eye and neck, sending her,
almost mercifully now, towards the end of her short life.

Suddenly, every bird was in flight and the clear morning
rang with sounds of their alarm as Rainha, spitting all the fire
of The Ages, reared onto the bank below her pup. Barking
loudly she made towards Rondo, but the pup, stunned into
shock by injury, heard nothing. Rainha began to haul up
towards the wounded youngster but stopped abruptly and
turned in fury after feeling something strike her on the back.
She saw the man standing in the boat and raced straight for
the water, for his arm was raised ready to throw another
missile onto Birthing Rock to clear the birds from the pup.
Rainha hit the water as a light, aluminium boathook arched
through the air to bounce on the summit and roll down to
within a few seal's lengths of the sea. The tin can which had
struck her on the back lay glinting beside the pup she had
just tried to save.

The man and his wife now joined to frighten off the
remaining Eye-Peckers which circled above the rock, throwing anything which came to hand, shouting and beating
loudly on the sides of their boat until the birds had all gone.
Through binoculars they looked at the pup and saw the
blood, the awful tear by her left eye and the pink, fleshy mess
of the deep wound on the back of her neck. The woman
cried in anger at the birds, tears damping her face as she
swore at them and even now not realising that, but for their
own ignorance and stupidity, none of this would have happened. Her husband tumbled forward and paid out all of the
spare anchor chain so Puffin would be carried back with the

flood to lie abreast of the rock and only a short distance from the wounded pup. Rainha watched in dismay as the boat drifted towards Rondo, then stopped as the man tied off the chain. She edged closer: the two people had their backs to her as they watched the pup, talking loudly as they discussed what they should do. The woman sobbed as she listened to Rondo's pitiful cries.

As she began to recover consciousness Rondo dragged air into her lungs, the world a blur and every breath, every shiver, filled with searing, dreadful pain. She was in deep shock, dehydrating rapidly and only hours from death. Although she bled little her wounds were terrible. The mother cow had to get to her quickly, but Puffin sat only a seal's length from the rock and Rainha knew she could not risk an attempt to get closer in case she herself might be killed. She floated motionless thirty seal's lengths from the boat as the couple jabbered indecisively, the man trying to reason with his wife about Rondo's fate. She wanted to take the seal aboard, bathe its wounds and nurse it. Her husband was against it, but she wore him down until at last he was forced to slide over the side of the boat, gasping in the cold water and splashing his way quickly onto Birthing Rock. Catching the rope his wife had thrown he pulled Puffin's stern as close as he dared then placed the line under a large boulder to secure it. He picked up the boathook he had thrown at the birds. His bare feet were being cut by sharp shells so he left the cans and other missiles they had thrown and took from his wife a large, canvas shopping bag. He opened it out, looking at it carefully and gauging its size before walking gingerly towards the pup.

Rondo was by now barely conscious, for the shock of pain had dulled her senses so that, although she heard every sound, she could make no sense of anything and was unable to react and make her escape. Her left side felt stiff and sore, and with each breath she took, no matter how short, pain followed air deep into her lungs making her exhale again quickly, shuddering in pain.

The man stood over the young seal and looked at her wounds. The sun beat heavily on the rock which burned the soles of his feet as he moved away from the pup's head to drop to one knee and see how he could bundle the small animal into the bag without hurting it. His wife shouted advice, and Rainha, seeing the man now so close to Rondo, moved closer, almost as far as the boat while the man fumbled, opening the bag wide and holding it next to the pup. Lifting Rondo's tail a little he eased the canvas over her limp form. She felt his hand under her belly and murmured in protest as he jerked slightly when turning the bag sideways so Rondo's body would lie along the bottom. He lifted the load to test it and the pup felt the canvas tighten around her. The bag swung as she was carried the short distance to the water's edge, bumping gently as the man released Puffin's rope from the boulder and tried to hold it tight at the same time as he stepped into the water.

The pup's weight drew the sides of the bag tight, crushing her. Awake only to the fact that she was captive she bawled in fright and tried in vain to move her limbs and escape. Rainha heard her cries and barked in the tongue of seals, telling her pup that she was close and to escape if she could. As he felt the icy loch grip his groin the man gasped and stumbled, and a foot slid from beneath him making him fall backwards in the water and let go the rope. Puffin drifted out a small way, no longer held against the shore, and the man, still gripping the bag, yelled loudly to his wife to hold out the boathook. Water flooded around Rondo as the man fumbled and the salt sea was like a spear in her wounds. She writhed with pain, desperate to break free, drawing great gulps of air and bawling loudly, now hanging half way out of the bag and close to freedom, only for the man to regain his footing and lift her, once again, out of the water. The pup caught sight of him and snarled, a new urgency making her twist and turn violently. He had let go of the boathook again, and was now able to lower his arm to push the pup's flayed head back inside her canvas cell. But as Rondo saw the flash of white flesh move towards her, her voice sang out in fury.

A long, pained cry rang out across the loch as the man's hand touched the pup, for as his grip had tightened close to her wounded eye she had turned. Feeling hairless flesh against her skin and sensing the rank, deadly smell of man, before he had been able to do more his wrist had been engulfed by the pup's jaw, the tiny, razor sharp teeth closing like a vice, puncturing skin and flesh and grinding on the bone of his left forearm. As he screamed in pain he fell, the breath taken from him by the desperate power of Rondo's bite.

Rainha's flight cry was in Rondo's ears, and as she tore her mouth from the man's arm she was already struggling blindly to free herself from the bag, driving with her rear flippers to get some purchase on the water. Her mother dived under the boat then surfaced and made for the rock at full pelt, brushing hard against the man and knocking him sideways as she passed. The woman saw her and screamed, fearing for her husband's safety, but Rainha was no threat, and in no more than a few seconds was pushing Rondo roughly, urgently, clear of Birthing Rock, swimming strongly with the pup almost draped over her head until they were a safe distance from the boat and its hapless, interfering crew. As the woman hauled her bleeding husband aboard, the cow stopped in the water. She sank below the pup, nuzzling her and holding up her head so she would take the mother scent. Weakly, but with confusion now beginning to fade, Rondo slithered on to Rainha's back and, leaving Puffin and her crew in noisy disarray, the two made off across Loch Shiel towards the rocky camouflage of North Shore.

Rondo was still on the cow's back as they came to a small, partially enclosed bay, the entrance to which was split into two channels by a jagged, arching reef called by men, The Cat's Back. The seabed was of fine, white sand which ran onto the shore to form a silver beach strewn with large, grey boulders. The beach sloped gently upwards, and above the tideline a grassy strip was surmounted by a steep, rocky bank overhung with bog myrtle and heather. The sand was firm under her belly as Rainha touched bottom, and after she had tipped the pup from her back, she pushed her through the shallowest water to the dry beach. The tide still had a short distance to rise and the cow kept just behind the youngster, pushing her gently upwards every few minutes as the water rose, so Rondo wasn't forced into any great effort. The pup was weak and must feed soon if she were not to sink too deeply into shock to allow any chance of recovery. She could barely struggle up the beach, but as the tide topped out the cow nudged harder, persisting until the pup had crawled slowly upwards and was settled behind a large boulder, shaded from the worst of the sun's heat and above the mark of the highest tides.

Rainha hauled to the pup's side, and as the youngster took the mother scent, her small reserve of energy drove her to the udder where she drank greedily, ignoring pain for a few minutes as the thick, yellow stream filled her belly and began the long fight to strengthen the fragile thread on which her life now hung. As Rondo suckled, Rainha heard the stutter of Puffin's engine, fading quickly now as the boat made off for the small town and its doctor. The cow raised her head to sniff the small breeze which had risen from the west. She smelled and listened, scanning the loch, but nothing stirred, and as the morning grew late and the injured pup finished her feed to lie exhausted beside her, Rainha, too, fell into a deep and thankful slumber.

As the day wore on the pup woke from time to time and drank. Remarkably, Rondo had sunk no further into shock and her mother's rich milk sustained her now as her body fought against the damage it had sustained under the beaks of the Eye-Peckers. Rainha looked down at Rondo's wounded head. The damage could be seen more plainly now, and apart from the deep neck wound at the base of her skull, two long, deep gashes crossed the pup's left eye, ragged and by now tightly stretched over a fierce swelling. Flesh lay exposed under the flayed skin, so that the effect was of a red, diagonal cross, centred by the pierced, black eye which even now had begun to cloud and shrivel, useless for the rest of whatever life the pup might have. It was a grave wound, and even an adult seal in full prime might have difficulty recovering from such an injury. The neck wound was not so bad, but anything could happen, and only time would tell if the Eye-Peckers were to be allowed to complete the work they had begun. Even if Rondo were to survive she

would have but one, single eye to guide her among the
lodges of Leaper and Tail Shaker. She must learn their ways
quickly, to stalk the whiting shoals and find the rocky dens
of conger and lobster and all the myriad other ways and
methods used by her Kind to keep their bellies full.
Northland winters are hard and sparsely spread with sustenance, and in only a few short months, Rondo must grow
and learn all these things, for a seal, like any bird or beast
needs to use to the full every gift bestowed on it by The
Ages, and injuries, however small, might easily thwart even
the simplest endeavour. The pup had little chance: only
Rainha's milk and care could keep her alive, and even then
she would need luck in greater quantity than was her right-
ful share. It might have been better had the Eye-Peckers
been able to finish their task, releasing Rondo One-Eye from
the misery to come.

That evening Rainha moved her pup the short distance to
Cat's Back Reef, for in the night hours, fox and badger
roamed and neither would turn down the opportunity to kill
the weakened youngster and fill their bellies. The cow
pushed Rondo down the sandy slope until she reached the
loch and floated naturally. Without thinking, the pup began
to swim, her rear flippers moving rhythmically as she stayed
close to the cow across the short distance to the arch of
jagged rock.

The clean, salt sea felt sharp as it washed over her wounds,
but after only a few minutes began to cool them, reducing
their fierce pain. Soothed a little, the pup swam beside her
mother who was careful to ensure that Rondo used as little
energy as possible. They hung in the water a little way from
the reef, watching for any danger until Rainha, satisfied the
place was safe, hauled onto the highest part of the rock and
watched as Rondo struggled up to lie beside her.

She fell fast asleep soon after her meal, draped like a small,
black sack over the top of the reef. Now Rainha was hungry.
The efforts of the past few days had sapped her energy and
she knew that the sick pup must be fed in full measure if it
were to hold its own, let alone recover. After a normal
birthing and with a healthy, uninjured pup, older cows might

not need to hunt hard for a few weeks, converting blubber to provide milk for their youngsters. But this was different, and Rainha left young Rondo on the reef then swam along North Shore towards Gull Rocks and The Village. After exploring fruitlessly a few places she knew well, the cow dived deep into a weedy hole and nosed about among waving fronds of kelp and wrack. A swirl of bottom mud; a sharp, cork-screwing turn and her teeth fell hard across the back of a big rock-cod which she carried quickly to the surface. She ate hungrily, holding the fish between her claw-tipped, front limbs as she floated on her back, tearing white flesh from bone.

Within an hour she had returned to the reef, murmuring gently as she approached and nuzzling the pup in reassurance as Rondo struggled clumsily to join her mother in the water. The pup suckled in the shallows, drinking for longer now as a glimmer of strength returned to her rested body, oblivious to pain for as long as milk ran freely. In fading light the seals hauled again onto the sandy strip of beach that had been their first refuge after their escape from Birthing Rock, Rondo's head throbbing as she made the effort to follow her mother up the slope. The numbing pain had returned making her feel dizzy, but with her belly now filled with Rainha's milk she was able to doze on the sand until the mercy of sleep carried her from pain.

*　*　*

The two seals remained at Cat's Back Bay, for it was a remote place where Rainha knew that they would not be disturbed. When the cow left to hunt or cool off she took the pup to the reef, which not only bathed her wounds with clean, salt water as she swam there, but kept her safe from fox or badger, and, should Eye-Peckers appear, the pup only had to roll sideways in order to tumble into the water. A fresh Atlantic breeze had robbed the sun of much of its killing power, and Rondo remained mercifully free of the flies which in still weather would have plagued her, carrying infection into her wounds. She was still very weak, despite feeding often, and each time her mother woke or returned from a hunting foray it would have been no surprise to her to find the pup dead. In the Way of The Ages, Rainha had no expectations, and only the accumulated purpose of all that had happened to her Kind since the days of The Seal Fathers brought her back, time and again, to tend her helpless youngster. Rondo, as The Ages demanded, bore her injuries with fortitude and suckled strongly whenever she could. For the first few days she showed little sign of improvement, but as her wounds began to heal and milk in plenty began to build flesh onto her young bones, little by little, she came back to life.

By the end of the first week, the mistiness which, for a week or two after birth, hampers the vision of young seals and other beasts until their eyes strengthen and grow used to light and dark, cleared, and Rondo began to see normally through the good, right eye which had developed, perhaps, more quickly than had her left eye remained uninjured. She began to recognise the things around her such as the arching sweep of the reef on which she sometimes rested, and the shape of Rainha's head as she swam towards the beach through the channel. She saw, too, the high bank which rose above the bay and even began to learn to angle her head a little to the left to compensate for the loss of the eye on that side. In all this time Rainha remained fit, maintaining her milk supply by hunting at night when Eye-Peckers were at roost, taking all and everything she could find. Leapers were few, for the land lay parched that year, and under the drought which afflicted it, rivers were all but dry. But despite this, every evening Shoals of Tail Shaker ran in and out of Loch Shiel, and Rainha took her share.

Rondo One-Eye grew stronger. Milk filled her and her body thickened as she swam daily in the shallows with her mother, her limbs moving more and more easily with every new tide as she learned to roll and spin and dive. As she learned she came to use less effort, less energy, and so, in the way of The Ages, more of the goodness of Rainha's milk was used to strengthen her further, not only building muscle, but growing clean, new tissue around her wounds and helping them heal more quickly. A growing independence came with her new strength, so sometimes she would leave the reef even if Rainha had not returned, swimming for a while in the shallows before hauling once again onto the beach. On one occasion, on a morning when the cow had still not returned three hours after sunrise, Rondo had fretted, hungry for milk, but after a while had dozed off. Waking suddenly she felt something touch her rear flippers and on turning saw two black backed gulls beside her which hopped back as she faced them. For a moment the pup was confused, still sleepy and not knowing whether to fight or make an escape, but The Ages spoke, and she charged down the beach faster than she had ever before travelled, driving hard with her rear limbs as she hit the water. She dived to the bottom then turned to look up. Seeing nothing through the cloud of sand and mud she had stirred up, she rose a little, lifting her nose and eyes above the surface. The birds had followed her and now wheeled noisily above so she dived again, swimming below the surface as far as the reef then turning again to look up as she reached the shallows. The water here was clear, and now her good eye focussed and she was able to see the gulls above. She stayed and watched, hanging just above the bottom. Within a few seconds both birds landed on the water, the closer almost directly above the pup. Memories of pain filled her mind. Visions of the cruel beak which had taken the sight of her left eye tightened every young muscle and the youngster was coiled, ready to strike.

The executioners remained above, waiting patiently for the unprotected pup to resurface. But they had not reckoned with the power of her memory, for Rondo had gathered all her small but growing strength and now, cheeks pulled back to bare her gums and teeth, she uncoiled, driving herself upward towards the nearest gull. Almost leaving the water as she broke surface and at the same time slashing sideways with her mouth she rolled heavily onto the bird, and with the large flight feathers of the lower part of a wing already between her teeth, she dragged the Eye-pecker below the loch. But her teeth slipped on the smooth feathers, and she twisted and lunged to try to take it across the back as she would a large fish as the bird paddled frantically with wings and webbed feet to reach the surface. Rondo, in youthful fury and without the benefit of two good eyes, lost touch with the bird and was left to follow as the gull broke away and gained sufficient purchase on the air to fly out of reach. She surfaced a short way from the reef, snarling and spitting at the birds which wheeled, shrieking, above her. They saw the tiny size of her; but more than that, above the bared gums and teeth they saw the mark over her left eye, the livid cross of Rondo One-Eye; and by that sign, they would remember her.

Rondo swam around in the bay almost daring the gulls to attack again, but for them it would be worth neither the energy nor risk of injury. The pup's anger kept her alert long after they had flown west, and she hauled onto the beach still growling infant sounds. As she calmed down again she had time to think. Rainha had still not returned and she began to fret, dozing fitfully then waking, hunger and insecurity growing in her. She mewed and whistled, hoping her signal would be heard on the loch, and then, her patience gone, took to the water, swimming a hundred seal's lengths outside the reef in an effort to locate her mother. Lonely, dejected and hungry, she trod water with her tail, lifting her head as far as she could above the surface and tilting it to give her good eye fullest scope to scan the loch. There was nothing. She looked aimlessly below the wavelets before searching yet again, squeaking helplessly.

She felt a swirl below and dropped her head quickly to search the deeps. She saw nothing until suddenly she was rolled on her back and cried out, bawling loudly in fear as a large black shape appeared beside her. Fright turned to joy as Rondo took the mother scent and the two seals weaved and tumbled until The Ages spoke and Rondo sought the udder. But Rainha made her work, racing off through the channel into the bay and waiting in the shallows as the pup followed, breathless and hungry. With the sun now high they hauled up. Rondo suckled strongly before dozing, then fell into a long, deep sleep, shaded by the mother cow.

A few hours later Rainha woke, and after scanning the

horizon, looked down at her sleeping pup. The cross cuts on her left eye were closing, tightening slowly so that when the wound healed no trace of the eye itself would be left. The pup had swum daily with Rainha in Cat's Back Bay and the clear sea had bathed the wounds, its salt helping to kill germs and purify. The eye wound still pained Rondo, and sometimes when the sun beat down on her body she would fret until the cow brought her to the loch and cooled the useless eye and its cruel wound. But now, far worse than the pierced eye was the deep hole on the back of Rondo's neck. The pain of it was ever present and the pup was becoming used to it, accepting it as part of her existence. It was not the searing pain she had felt when her eye had been stabbed open, but a dull, numb tightness of skin and flesh, for the beak of the Eye-pecker which had made the wound had been tainted by the rotting carcase of a stillborn deer calf, and the hole in Rondo's neck was becoming a deep, poisonous well from which seeped evil smelling, yellow fluid. For a few days the ragged hole had almost closed and the pup had coped well, perhaps more preoccupied by the pain of her eye, but now the infection was rooted deep in the flesh of her neck where the cleansing, salt sea could not reach. It threatened to spread quickly through her system, turning all her blood as bad and poisonous as the wound itself so that even all the richness of Rainha's milk would never save her. The cow leaned closer to Rondo, and holding her nose above the pup's head, sniffed gently at the pus that wept from her youngster's wound. She knew it was the stench of death and that there could be one, single cure. Risky though it was, if Rondo were to live she had to be moved to a place where the poison might be drawn out and the neck wound could heal. She might perish on the way, for with the wound's poisons growing stronger by the hour she would weaken quickly and drift into shock. Nevertheless, the cow knew by The Ages what must be done and slept now, resting before the task.

Chapter 5: The Silver Thread

From earliest times the women of Loch Shielside had used the sea weed called kelp to bandage the wounds inflicted on their men by bear or wild boar, or in their battles against other tribes. In times of plagues, or when boils or running sores afflicted them, kelp was boiled in cauldrons and the fluid used in poultices to draw the badness from poisoned flesh. Through all this time, the long reef off the Southern side of Sword Island where kelp grew more abundantly than in any other place was famous in the Northlands, and was known simply as The Healing Reef. For the seals, too, it had for long been a place of healing: and longer than for men, for remember, seals had lived in Loch Shiel since before man learned to stand straight or to throw sticks at wolves, and many were the seal wounds healed there since the days of The Seal Fathers.

An ancient legend of men connected seals with Healing Reef, for from the Village at the head of Loch Shiel that overlooked Bay of Shelters, men had watched seals rolling in the yellow fronds at low tide, and had believed for longer than anyone could remember that those beasts, ailing from some injury or sickness, were curing themselves among the weed.

The story told of how the seals had first taught man to use kelp. It came from when mens' battles were still fought with stone axes and bone-tipped spears and before he wrote in any way but by drawing pictures on the walls of caves. And the tale was from a time before man's greatness had led him from the old ways, and might have been lost but for a more recent time, more than two hundred years before Rondo lived, when, during a period of great turmoil, the way men lived began to change forever. It was a time of blood and strife; a time of broken promises and one when brother fought against brother and father against son. It was, too, the time seals first heard the rattle of muskets, and watched in dread as fire spread across the slopes of Dun Mountain.

On the wide flood plain of Rough River there had been a great gathering of men who had risen to fight for a young Prince who had come from France to regain the throne taken from his father by a foreign king. Fearful of rebellion in the Northlands, the new king's soldiers who were garrisoned nearby had searched every lonely glen and lochside dwelling for the weapons they felt sure were being gathered for use in the prince's cause. In the Village by Loch Shiel, soldiers looked suspiciously towards Healing Rock and its long, yellow reef. Villagers told them that the island was ridden with plague and that all who went there would surely die, but they grew suspicious, and a party of dragoons went one day to the island and searched it thoroughly. But the store of muskets and swords was well hidden in a deep, covered pit, and the soldiers, finding nothing, returned to sup wine and ale outside the inn. A day later two of their number were dead, their tongues so red and grotesquely swollen that their mouths could not be closed before they were buried.

The innkeeper's poison had ensured that soldiers went no more to Healing Rock, and every moonless night men and women crossed Bay of Shelters in boats with muffled oars to pass weapons into the store. Hidden under a cover of bracken and pine branches, the arsenal grew until at last the Prince arrived from France and his clans gathered above the green flood plain of Rough River to take arms and follow him into the south.

The following month, September, many seals were gathered in Loch Shiel to await the autumn run of Leaper and Tail Shaker into the rivers of their birth. But few came at that leaf-fall and throughout the winter which followed many seals went hungry, appearing so thin and listless that even the people of the Village noticed their plight.

Early the following year, after snowmelt but before the

main greening of spring, the prince's cause fell under the
grapeshot of the king's cannon at a bloody battle in the east.
Fearsome was the plunder of the Northlands after the defeat
of the clans. Men, women and children, from the oldest to
those still in their mothers' arms were slaughtered throughout
the summer, and houses and whole villages were burned to
ash. To Loch Shielside, where the rising had begun, was
brought a special, merciless revenge. The Village was razed to
the ground, and those who escaped before being murdered in
their beds were forced to live like wild beasts on the hill.

Throughout this time, with the screams of their kin ringing in their ears and the smoke of burning houses drifting
over the loch to where they were hidden, two of the Prince's
chieftains, both gravely wounded, lay in the covered pit on
what was now being called The Island of Swords. They had
been too badly injured to endure months of journeying so
had elected instead to take their chance by hiding in the
former arsenal, placing their wounds and future safety under
the care of a trusted kinswoman who had told them she was
confident the soldiers would not search the island.

Every night she could, she came to them with milk, oat-
meal and cheese, and as the chiefs ate she went to the Healing
Reef and cut long fronds of Kelp with which to dress their
wounds. Slowly they recovered. A ship was found to take
them to France, and every night they waited for the signal
light to warn them of the boat's approach. One evening they
saw something flicker far down the loch below the west peak
of Dun Mountain. They made their way down the steep
bank to where the Kelp reef meets Sword Island and sat,
wrapped in their thick, dark plaids, in a place where long
heather overhung them and broke their outline.

A big moon rose above The Narrows and cast a beam of
silver along the loch towards the waiting chiefs. The water
shimmered, and high above Loch Shiel every mountain ridge
was etched against the sky, causing the fugitives to worry lest
their rescuers be picked out, silhouetted by the moon as they
rowed from the anchored vessel to collect them. They
prayed for cloud but the moon grew ever brighter and rose
higher and higher in the western sky. What if there were

soldiers on the move, they thought, for if they heard even the sound of well muffled oars, it would be easy to pick out a boat on the loch so clear had it become. They huddled closer to the rock and listened for the slightest sound. Suddenly, there was a splash below them some way out on the water and their hands fell to their sword hilts as they rose, ready to fight for their lives. But it was no dragoon; no red coated soldier with musket trained, for there, lying in the kelp under the moon's lantern was a pale, shining seal, one good, clear eye looking straight towards them, the other blind, its socket covered by a deep, diagonally scarred cross.

Each gripped the rock, trembling in fear, for the shape of that cross lying on its side they knew to signify a mystic power men called the second sight. The seal moved towards them, ghost like, its coat silver under the moon and its head held high as though it were about to speak. Frozen, the warriors watched then gasped in awe as the seal stopped close to them, for now, below the jagged cross over the beast's left eye there appeared a running sore, deep and red, glowing as though fired by some unseen flame.

Consumed with fear now, one rose, and tearing a crucifix from the chain around his neck he held it aloft towards the ghostly animal. But the seal did not move. It seemed almost to smile, then rolled, giving a long, piercing bark before turning again to look once more at the men then disappearing soundlessly and without the slightest ripple.

A few days later the chiefs boarded their ship and sailed for France. Through all their years in exile they wondered at the omen they had seen and spoke of it only in whispered voices. On a bright autumn day seventeen years later the chiefs returned, now fully pardoned. Beneath the golden leaves of Owl Oaks they landed on the shore and went in search of the kinswoman who had saved them so many years ago. Being led to her they gave her gifts and thanked her for their lives. They asked after her health for she was old and frail, but she reassured them with her sharpness of mind and they went on to talk of their years in exile and their hope and happiness now they had returned to their own country. As the sun sank, all three went to the inn and sat outside to sip whisky and watch the mellow colours of the evening hills. Looking over Bay of Shelters to the pines of Sword Island where they had been hidden, they told the old woman what they had seen there.

Puffing an old clay pipe she listened as they told the strange tale. Their voices were hushed as they spoke, almost as though they feared the seal's return as they sat looking out towards the place where they had seen the beast so many years ago. At the end of the tale the woman sat for a while, staring out across the loch, then, turning towards them, asked to hear the story once again.

They told her again of the wound and the livid running sore which had shone gently but with such power and strength, and how fearless of them the beast had been, how calm, as though knowing it could not be harmed. What could it have been, they asked. Where had it come from? Was it the Water Horse of ancient legend? She gazed over the loch. No, she said, it had not been the Water Horse. She knew what it was, she said, but had only heard the story once as a child and would have to think carefully. Slowly, she began the almost forgotten tale which had been handed down over countless centuries.

*   *   *

In an ancient time there had been a young chief who lived on the banks of Rough River. He loved the land in which he lived and knew the ways of every bird and beast. He was fair and handsome, fleet and strong, a skilled hunter and a patient cultivator of crops. Such became his greatness in his own country, that as he entered manhood his people forgot his given name and called him, Harvester.

One day a great ship came into the loch and anchored near the Village in Boat Bay. The ship carried a Messenger of The Ages, and his cry rang through the hills and over the waters of Loch Shiel as he called together the chiefs of the three great families of the earth. From the wide sky he called the eagle, from the land he summoned man, and, from the black, impenetrable deeps he sought the seal.

The heads of these three families gathered near the ship, Talon the eagle, largest and most powerful of her Kind, clasped her feet to the bough of a pine. The old she seal, Phoca, lay quietly in the shallows, and between the seal and the eagle, the young prince, Harvester, stood on the strand. All three knew each other well and were at ease, for land and sea had nourished all without conflict.

The Messenger of The Ages gave his news and then, sensing friendship between the three, praised them, eagle, seal and man, and told them to maintain the earth in plenty that all might continue to flourish; their sons and daughters, and their children, and all who came after them. To help them, to each who could satisfy him of a good purpose, the Messenger would give a length of magic, Silver Thread.

First, he called the seal and asked the wise old beast what she would do with the thread. She swam slowly towards the galley, thinking carefully. Stopping a few seal's lengths from the Messenger, she looked up and began to speak quietly in the tongue of her Kind.

"I will take your gift to a long, low reef close to my Resting Rock." she said. "There I will fasten it below the waves so it may grow long and thick in the salt sea, and Leaper and Tail Shaker will make their lodges there. Lobster and conger will seek the cover of its long strands, and should it flourish greatly my Kind shall use it also to heal our wounds and restore us to good health, so that in times of dearth or of sickness it shall both provide our food, and heal us."

The Messenger was well pleased and turned next to the eagle, saying, "And what of you, Long Wings – if I give you this magic thread, how will you use it for your Kind?"

The eagle launched herself from the bough, soared easily to the ship and landed, proud and fearless on the wide rail close to the Messenger. The golden bird fixed him with her eye, and in the tongue of eagles spoke softly. "I must view my kingdom before I answer. Will you wait for me a short while?" "Yes, I will wait, gladly." replied the Messenger, and the eagle took to the air. She beat her golden wings, rising higher and higher above them all, circling towards the sky until soon she was above Dun Mountain and all the other hills and could see far beyond The Narrows and The Islands Of Lorne, and could no longer be seen by the seal and the young prince, so high had she flown.

The seal, Phoca, waited patiently, preening herself, occasionally looking below the surface towards the loch bottom in case she might spot something she could catch later. But Harvester fretted and grew impatient, and soon he shouted over the water to the Messenger. "Will you not hear me now, before the eagle returns, – I have made my choice and know already what I will do with your gift!" But the Messenger held up his hand, bidding Harvester to wait, and think more on the use of the magic thread.

After some time the eagle returned, alighting again gracefully on the rail and fixing the Messenger with her strong, honest eye. "I have looked upon my kingdom, Messenger, I have decided on my purpose". she said quietly. "Speak, Golden Head – tell me what you would do". "I will take your gift of Silver Thread from here" said the bird, "and I will carry it to the place where a small spring rises in the corrie that lies between the two peaks of Dun Mountain. There, with these talons that can crush the skull of deer or fox, I will clench the Thread deep into the bed of that spring where it rises from the earth. Its magic will enrich the water of the spring so that even in the driest summer the corrie will be lush and green, providing food and water for every bird and beast, and if all these things may eat and drink then they will also thrive and multiply, and my Kind, too, shall flourish."

"During every winter " continued the eagle, "long grasses, heather shoots and seeds, though withered, shall still provide food for the hares and grouse which feed us through the dark months. And before snowmelt my own Kind shall draw the softest woodrush from the ground to line the mighty baskets that are our nests, keeping our eggs and young warm even in the coldest blasts of the Northlands."

"Your Kind will prosper under such a purpose." said the Messenger, "I am satisfied: go now to your bough and wait."

Even as the bird took flight the prince had begun once more to shout across the water.

"Hear me now, Messenger," he cried. "for with your gift

of Thread I shall weave a magic net. It will be invisible to Leaper and Tail Shaker, and from every snowmelt to the last leaf-fall my net shall reap, filling the storehouses of my Kind against the dearth of our winters." The Messenger raised his hands high above his head. "I am satisfied." he said. "With all of you I am satisfied – but hear me well – listen as you have not listened before, for with each gift of Silver Thread I am instructed by The Ages to attach one, single condition."

All listened well as the Messenger explained. As he gave each a length of Thread and told them to guard it carefully, he said also that it was to be used only for the purpose each of them had spoken of to The Messenger and no other. If used in any other way, the Thread would destroy all that it touched. They thanked the Messenger and asked what they might give in return, but he would take nothing from them, saying that all he needed was their trust. He made ready his galley, and summoning the east wind to carry him seaward, made off down Loch Shiel into the west leaving the trees sighing behind him.

When he had gone, seal and eagle went their separate ways to use the gift of The Ages as they had promised, each taking care not to be seen by any other bird or beast as they performed their duty to the Messenger. But Harvester left the shore happily, whistling as he made his way through Owl Oaks, seeing none of his people who, hiding among the trees and bushes, had watched and listened as he shouted to the Messenger.

All flourished on Loch Shielside. A great kelp bed formed along the low reef and the seals hunted there when food was scarce. They learned also to use the Kelp to heal themselves when sick or wounded, or when they became ridden with parasites. And it was kind to them, for it had in its long yellow fronds every cure known to The Ages. And from Dun Mountain the bird of gold could look out over the corrie floor in any season and see it move with life. All manner of creatures drank from the stream, bathed in its clear runnels and fed among the verdure that it nourished.

The people of the Village grew fat under the weight of

Leaper and Tail Shaker which hung, dried and cured, filling their barns. Harvester was careful of his net, keeping it always tied to his waist in a strong purse made from the pelt of a mountain hare. He grew famous and men travelled many miles to watch him work his net at the mouth of Rough River where it ran into the loch. Many flattered the young chief, and when some grew jealous, wanting the magic net for themselves, Harvester would frighten them by casting the net at the stump of a dead tree, making it crack and belch with smoke, all as The Messenger had foretold.

As his fame grew, when crops failed in other parts, men came to Loch Shielside to ask Harvester's help, knowing him to be good and generous. He did his best to feed all who asked, but some grew greedy, taking their honest share tenfold and more. As the years passed the Prince was forced to work many hours each day to keep such numbers fed. He lost the skills of his youth, grew tired and began to worry about trifling matters. His humour faded as his work increased, and in time the confidence and friendship of his people waned, then died. And then, one spring day, there came to Loch Shielside a rich merchant from the Southlands.

Taking a house close to The Village, he entertained all those he thought might be of use to him. The merchant wished to trade in Leapers, for so great had become the Prince's fame that he had heard of Harvester far to the south. He tried to befriend the Prince, but he was still proud and turned down the man's requests to meet, saying he would have nothing to do with trade, for the Messenger of The Ages had forbidden all such things. But the merchant was patient, and settling down to wait, sent for his only daughter to come from the Southlands to tend his household.

Harvester continued to fish with his net of Silver Thread, but now, ever less and less Leapers and Tail Shakers survived its mesh to make the long passage to the spawning grounds in the highest reaches of Rough River. His was a great burden, for with an ever growing number to feed he was forced to travel further and further from the Village to find sufficient Leapers to meet their demand. So far, though, the Prince had worried little about the shortage, for he had come to believe his flatterers, and by now thought himself as someone quite apart from others. Anyway, he thought, it was good to get away from The Village sometimes, for it allowed him to think of the old days when he had been happier. And all the while his people cheated him, secretly selling Leaper and Tail Shaker to the merchant and any others who would buy.

One day Harvester had travelled far down Loch Shiel in his canoe in search of fish. He had spent much time that day pondering his lot, for recently Leapers had been even harder to find and he had become perplexed. He had looked for a reason for the shortage, for there had been no fish at all in places where he would normally expect to find at least a few. At midday he laid on a bank above the shore and slept awhile, then wakened to see a seal gnawing at the carcase of a large Leaper only a few spear's lengths from him. Angry, he leapt up shouting at the beast, which disappeared, frightened by the outburst. Here was the reason, thought Harvester, the seals, they must be the cause of this dearth of fish. The seals; that had to be it. He caught few Leapers that day which served only to confirm his suspicions, but late in evening when he returned home, all thought of fish and seals was driven from his mind. The merchants daughter had arrived, and never before had such beauty been seen in the Northlands.

Fair and innocent, without guile or worldliness was the maid. When she spoke it was as though each small, mountain bird gave voice as one, and when she moved it was as a swan on some clear and brilliant pool. The people of The Village called her, Rainha, which in the tongue of their race means, queen-like. And they thought, of course, that she must have been sent there for their Prince; an omen perhaps, a gift from The Ages to reward his work in feeding them and swelling their purses. But despite his constant wooing and the exhortations of her father that she should take up with him, the maid would have nothing to do with Harvester, saying he had lost his skills to flattery, and that without his magic net he would be nothing.

The Prince was devastated. Besotted with the maid he walked the shore, desolate, inconsolable in his grief as he lamented the day he had ever taken the gift of Silver Thread. He saw The Man Bird soaring effortlessly above Dun Mountain and was angry that the eagle should enjoy such peace and good living when he himself was now so much reduced. He wanted to cast his net at the eagle, not so much to destroy it, for Harvester was not an evil man, but more to remove the bird from sight so it would remind him no more of his ill fortune. But The eagle flew too high, so he vented his anger in even more stupid ways, casting the net at great boulders, making them crack like thunder as they split apart.

On a clear autumn morning, close to the place where the Messenger's galley had anchored, Harvester saw a seal in the loch with a great Leaper in its jaws. Seeing the silver fish, all his anger and resentment boiled and he began to stalk the seal, bent on its destruction. The beast had no real reason to be suspicious, for all had lived in peace there in the memory of every bird and beast, so it remained happily on the surface chewing the pink flesh of the salmon.

The Prince grew closer but the beast remained where it was, and only as Harvester drew level did it see his arm arc over his head as the net was cast out over the water. The seal threw the Leaper to one side and rolled, trying to dive, but before it could make its escape it screamed in pain so loudly, and so like the cry of a young girl, that for a moment Harvester's blood ran cold. He looked out to where the seal writhed to free itself. Over its left eye was a smoking, livid cross where the mesh of the net had caught it. The seal escaped, but Harvester knew that it would soon die because the net had touched it. The beast would take no more of his Leapers and Tail Shakers, and its fearful cry soon became lost to his memory.

*   *   *

But after the death of the seal the shortage of Leapers continued. The Prince still wooed the merchant's daughter but she spurned him always, repeating what she had said before. And his people did not revere or trust him as they once had, for even though they had grown to depend so heavily on the

Prince they had become lazy, and now, when their bellies were empty, they had little will to provide for themselves and spent their time instead, watching Harvester and complaining about him.

Obsessed with the maid, the Prince now spent much of his time plotting to entrap her. Rainha's father had been cunning, making Harvester believe that he could make his daughter agree to marry him if he would agree to exchange all his lands for her. He would arrange for the maid to be tricked into marriage, he said. He would pay a priest, and when all was done Harvester could carry the girl far to the south where another sea could fall to his net and make him rich enough to buy back his lands and return to his own country. The prince of Loch Shielside was overjoyed, for the Messenger of The Ages had said nothing of where he should use the net, only in what purpose it was to be cast.

When she saw the Prince, her father and the priest in the barn to which she had been tempted, Rainha knew at once what was about to happen. She screamed and ran for the door but Harvester laughed and she knew the way must be blocked. She stood in the middle of the barn panting with rage. There was fire in her eyes and the priest cowered as the merchant pleaded with her to no avail. "No." she cried out. "No, – never – never."

She flew at the Prince with her arms flailing. He held up his hands to avoid her blows. She did not strike him, but used his shoulder as a lever with which to help her leap onto the makeshift altar and from there, spring for the open skylight. Harvester and the maid's father scrabbled in the dim light, desperate to prevent her escape, but she was nearly there, and one strong push would see her clear and free.

But it was not to be. The Prince shouted to her but she would not listen and did not falter in her flight. But as she made her final, gasping effort to escape the maid screamed a long, unearthly scream, for wrapped around her, burning, tearing at her, scalding flesh, blood and bone, was the Prince's net of Silver Thread. She fell to the dirt floor, her gown charred and in tatters, her once lovely form smoking and smouldering. Her father and the priest, believing themselves to be in mortal danger, smashed down the door and fled, leaving Harvester with his dying love.

He cried out for help and the best healing woman of the Village came to tend the maid. When she saw the girl she knew at once the cause was hopeless and knelt close to Rainha, cradling her head, waiting for her death. Harvester pled with her, asking her to try anything, if only to bring the girl to consciousness so he could tell her how sorry he was for his wickedness. Rainha was taken to the Healing Woman's house among the ancient trees of Owl Oaks and laid on a bed of woodrush. The Woman did all she could using all the cures and remedies she had ever learned, but knew in her heart the maid would never recover. She and her helpers made potions and ointments, but nothing cured the awful burns and Rainha's beauty faded making her appear older and older as life slipped from her.

Harvester's grief was boundless. He wandered hill and shore cursing all things, casting his net at trees and rocks destroying everything he saw. Only when the land around was bare and nothing more lived did he cease his destruction. He cursed the net but would not part with it despite the counsel of the wisest in The Village. As he saw clearly now all the things he had left undone since receiving the Gift his despair grew. Everything was gone. No crops grew in his once fertile fields and his land was barren. The buildings of The Village and the stone dykes which surrounded it had fallen into disrepair and crumbled more with every winter. But worst of all, no Tail Shaker and no great, Silver Leaper ran the falls of Rough River.

The Healing Woman came to him as he sat by the loch and told him that the maid was weakening and would surely die that day. Before rising and going to her he looked out over Loch Shiel. Where once he had seen beauty he now saw only desolation. The spirit was gone out of him and all life that was worth being lived was gone. As he wept, he heard a strange voice which spoke in his own tongue, asking, "Why do you weep, Harvester?"

Looking up, wiping tears of shame, sorrow and self pity from his eyes he saw the vision of a seal, an ancient beast.

Deep across the skin where its left eye should have been was a dreadful, burned brand; two wide, ragged weals in the form of a fallen cross.

Harvester reached for his net thinking the seal might mean to harm him, but before he could cast it the beast spoke again, asking the Prince if he had not killed and destroyed enough. He stared hard, for there was something uncannily familiar about the animal, but his mind was so full of trouble that nothing would fall into place.

"Why do you weep, here by the loch that is home to my Kind?" asked the seal. And as it spoke he realised which beast it must be that lay in the shallows a few seal's lengths from him. "You!" He said. "You; how do you still live? You were touched by my net. How do you live when my love lies dying, burned by the same Silver Thread that burned you: how can this be?" "I live" said the seal, "cured by the gift of The Messenger of The Ages, for it has flourished, and has healed the wounds of all my Kind since the day the Messenger called we three to the shore."

"You – you were there that day?"

"How your Kind forgets so easily Harvester! Yes it was I, for I am Phoca, Elder of my Kind who has borne storms and famines in great number. I took the Messenger's gift and placed it on the reef as I had promised."

"I remember little of that day, now." said Harvester. "And what does it matter, for my land is barren and my love lies dying. I have nothing. My life is done."

"Why did you try to kill me?" asked the beast, softly. "To kill you? – I cast my net at you because you plundered my Leapers."

"Your Leapers! Do you remember nothing of The Messenger's warning? Did he not tell us that his gift came to us only for our harmony; because all here lived in peace? Did he not order us to keep the earth in plenty? – Where is your plenty, Harvester, Prince of Loch Shielside? Where are your Silver Leapers and your Tail Shakers? And if they were yours and yours only, why then did you not maintain them and take only for your needs. Why did you not heed the Messenger?"

"I do not remember, old seal. I know only my grief." The
Prince's head was bowed and he was weeping. "If I have
done as you say then I am sorry. I am deeply sorry that I
tried to kill you and have blinded you. Our Leapers come no
more to Rough River as you say. It is all true and I am sorry,
but it is too late, – too late for anything."

The Prince fell silent and then stood, ready to go to say his
last farewell to Rainha. He tried to smile at the seal, but the
one-eyed beast said no more, only stared a wide, soft stare at
him as though in pity. Harvester turned and began to walk
slowly towards Owl Oaks.

"Wait! – wait Harvester, hear what I will tell you."

He turned and looked back towards the seal. "I have no
time, – I must go to the maid I have killed. And then, – then
I must take my own life for what I have done, for I can bear
to live no more." "Your maid may yet live, Prince of Loch
Shielside. Your maid may live and so, too, may your land
still flourish. Our Leapers and Tail Shakers may return also,
but first, there are certain things you must do."

Harvester ran to the waters edge. "What would you have
me do?" he cried, "Tell me now and I will carry out your
wish."

The seal told Harvester that he must first unravel the net
of Silver Thread so it would become useless, then cast it into
Loch Shiel so the tide might carry it far out to sea. When he
had done that the beast spoke again.

"Now, you must make a promise – and only if you do that
and hold firm to it will I instruct you in how to save these
things that you hold dear but have put in ruin through the
greed and foolishness of your Kind. Only by doing this can
you live in peace once more."

With new hope in his heart Harvester was eager to do
Phoca's bidding. The promise was to be held not only by
Harvester but by all his Kind, and for all time. It was a
simple thing, for all that the seal asked was that the Prince's
Kind would never again take more than their needs of bird,
beast or blade, but would harvest only those things necessary
to feed and clothe and comfort them.

The Prince agreed readily, but the old seal looked at him

firmly, saying, "Keep this promise Harvester; keep it faith-
fully, and if you do your Kind will flourish. But if you break
this oath my Kind shall suffer and the Kind of Talon who
soars above us now to hear you swear to this. And as we
suffer we will return to haunt you, and terrible will be our
anger and our revenge should you or any of your Kind not
remain true to us."

Once again Harvester gave his promise and begged the
seal to make haste and tell him how he was to save the maid.
He was told to fetch the Healing Woman who tended
Rainha. When she came, the seal dismissed the chief, telling
him he must know nothing of how the maid was to be
treated but go immediately and put his people to cultivating
the land and learning its ways again.

When he had gone Phoca spoke quietly to the Healing
Woman, and then, making sure no other person was watching, she climbed on to the seal's back and they made off
together towards the long reef where the kelp grew. When
the woman returned to the village it was with a great basket
of the healing weed, which she hid before making off
through Owl Oaks, now carrying a water pitcher, to the
rough path which led to Dun Mountain. Where the track
forked, Talon was waiting to carry her to the source of the
spring where the eagle had set down The Ages' gift. She
showed the Healer where to fill her pitcher with water from
the stream and instructed her in its use. After carrying her
back to the fork in the track, Talon wished her good fortune
then soared away across the corrie, leaving the Healing
Woman to return to The Village and begin her task.

Doing as seal and eagle had told, she dressed Rainha's
wounds with potions made using the kelp and springwater.
For days there was no change, and Harvester grew angry,
believing that the seal might have cheated him. But then, one
morning when the Healer went to Rainha's side, she found
the maid awake.

Slowly, as her wounds healed, Rainha was once more able
to walk by the shore and in the woods. Harvester kept clear
of her, for his shame was as deep as his love for the maid and
he could not bring himself even to approach her, knowing he

must be content to watch her from a distance, wondering at the beauty he would now, never, see more closely.

But Rainha, too, was watching, and began now to see Harvester in a different way. With his net gone he worked hard to regain his boyhood skills and put them to use for his people. Her father, never seen since the maid was burned, had been an evil man, and though the prince had been weak to fall in with him, perhaps, she thought, his suffering had made a man of him. – And he was handsome now, his locks were gold as straw and his face, tanned and healthy, was without the lines of worry he had had before. Soon, she had fallen in love with him.

They were married, and in all the years that followed, the Princess gave herself to healing and was loved by all the people of Loch Shielside. She had great power, speaking often with seals and birds and telling of times to come and harvests yet unsown.

It grew dark outside the inn as the kinswoman of the two chiefs finished her story, and the air had autumn's chill. They were still puzzled, and asked the old woman what they had seen that night by The Island Of Swords and why the wound over the seals eye was bare and running.

"It's strange, isn't it why her wound has never healed " she said. "So remember the promise of Harvester. Remember always, you and all who follow you, how he promised the seal that not only he, but all his Kind would take only what they needed from this earth."

Chapter 6

They had swum the long miles from Cat's Back Bay, and as the seals turned into Bay of Shelters Rondo was tired and weakening quickly. Rainha checked the loch then made straight for Resting Rock, shepherding the pup beside her and hauling onto the great slab only a few lengths so Rondo was not over-taxed. The pup suckled weakly, drinking as much as she could before exhaustion drove her to sleep.

Rainha woke as daylight strengthened and, almost immediately, caught the stench of the pup's neck wound. Shuffling round she looked out over Bay of Shelters and at its long, curving shore. The land, long starved of rain, was dry. Where there was no shade of any kind it had become brittle and cracked, and shrubs and grasses had taken a brownish tinge as they burned, day after day, under the sun, and the earth beneath them seemed to shrink as though in pain. Rough River, too, was almost dry and ran not as a Northland river should, gold and silver with a joyful sound, but lay in darkening, slime-filled pools, sliding reluctantly below the alders as if unwilling to seek its course to where it trickled indolently over the boulders and slabs into Bay of Shelters. Even the Bay itself possessed a barren look, and as a morning air no stronger than a rabbit's breath passed over the head of Loch Shiel, its surface, which should have been scattered with the ringed rise marks of Leaper and Tail Shaker, lay flat and calm as a sheet of waxed glass.

Rondo lay still, painlessly asleep as her mother began to clean herself. The cow shook herself heavily, ridding her coat of some of the salt which had dried into it, then scratched, while at the same time checking the Bay and its shoreline for anything unusual. She greeted two other beasts as they hauled up to bask. Only the drone of bees broke the silence and the sun was already hot. A few seals cruised lazily on the far side of the loch below the Village, and Rainha watched them until, from the mouth of Rough River a noisy tumult of splashing made her look up to see a stranger, not one of her own Kind but a pale beast with a long, straight nose and narrow head. The seal rolled and dipped, splashing with a front flipper, then stood on its tail, head up, looking towards Resting Rock. Rainha knew the animal to be of the Kind of the Seal Father, Halichus, who had made their homes in the great deeps of the Atlantic, wandering for most of their lives, hauling out on the most isolated, rocky shores only to moult and bear their young.

Rainha slid quietly past her sleeping pup and swam straight across the Bay towards the intruder. The water was clear and the cow dived, halting a few seal's lengths from the stranger to hang motionless just below the surface, looking at the beast. The pale coloured seal dropped its head and rolled slowly downwards, murmuring in the tongue of her Kind an ancient greeting she knew by The Ages Rainha would recognise. Twisting and rolling elegantly, she circled the cow, always keeping her distance and taking care to show no sign of aggression. At length, when Rainha was satisfied there was no threat from the newcomer and she turned and made off towards Resting Rock and her sickly pup, the grey cow made no attempt to follow.

She looked back as she hauled, knowing the stranger was young and meant no harm; but she remained suspicious and watchful as Rondo, now awake and squeaking, took her early feed. The journey had exhausted the young seal, and though normally she would not have been forced to travel such a distance until at least a few weeks old and stronger in limb and spirit, this was no ordinary time. She showed no outward signs of illness other than her wounds and was alert and bright, but the stink of death was with her, and though she herself had no sense of it, her life hung delicately in the balance.

★   ★   ★

The mother cow sniffed at the air knowing that if there were no wind that day there would be an army of flies to lay eggs in Rondo's wound. There might be Eye-Peckers, too, if the pup showed signs of weakening, for they were the first to sense every smallest tremor in the lives of other Kinds. She might have to move the pup once again to some small, sheltered bay where they could lie together in the shallows, for Rondo still needed rest before Rainha took her to the kelp which could be her only cure. The pup was asleep now after her feed, but when she woke, her mother knew that they would have to move.

A few hours later Rondo wakened to the noise of closing doors and car engines, drifting across Bay of Shelters from the Village as people began to go about their work. For some minutes she was frightened and restless, shuffling closer to her mother as the sun touched her neck and filled her with pain. A cormorant swam by and the pup, quickly ignoring her discomfort, watched avidly, tilting her head so that her right eye had full scope to see the bird. She had tensed almost as though about to pounce and the bird sensed this and dived, leaving the pup puzzled, grunting in low tones. Moving away from her mother she headed towards the water then stopped to sniff the air. The stench of her own wound filled her nostrils and she sneezed in shock, causing pain to return after the brief distraction of the cormorant's passage. She was beginning to feel it hard now; a throbbing pain, and twisted her head violently, trying to scratch her neck with a front flipper as though this might rid her of it and set her free from torment. She whimpered softly, and in a few seconds Rainha was beside her, pausing only to nudge the pup towards the cooling sea.

She had weighed carefully Rondo's tiredness, but knew there could be only one way, for if flies entered the wound, soon maggots would hatch and begin to feed on the young seal's flesh. She would lose energy as all the goodness of Rainha's milk went to fight the poison already in her and repair the damage done by the maggots. It would be more than she could cope with, and without the energy to feed she would dehydrate rapidly, drift into shock and enter a deep, unending sleep.

Chapter 7

Together, the two seals swam slowly around Sword Island towards its western edge. In a few minutes they would be among the streaming yellow weeds which held the key to Rondo's young life.

The kelp was smooth, almost oily. In places it had become entwined and moved slowly in the current in beckoning, silent ululation. Rainha rolled on her back as they entered the weed, twisting and rubbing, urging the pup to follow and copy her, but for a while Rondo could not understand and was suspicious of the long, waving stuff. Patiently, the cow continued, allowing her youngster to become used to the yellow forest and follow her, first around its thinner edges then moving towards the denser areas. Rondo soon became bored and began to lag behind. The cow disappeared, rising quickly to the surface and diving again on the far side of the reef's central ridge until she was at the edge of the kelp, half hidden but with a clear view. She listened carefully and heard the infant's squeaks as Rondo began to feel lost and started to panic, but she stayed where she was, out of sight of the pup.

Rondo began to search, swimming among the thicker beds and pushing her nose into cracks and spaces. She turned her head frequently to give her good eye scope and began to roll occasionally through three hundred and sixty degrees in order to catch any movement around her. Her panic died quickly after she began to search, for The Ages led her, willing her to find her mother. But after a time, when she had seen or heard nothing of the cow she became despondent and floated slowly to the surface, fear, once again beginning to increase its grip.

The pup lay still with her head under water, scanning the seabed. She had heard the mother call and knew Rainha must be close. A small cloud of sand puffed from the bottom close to the edge of the weed. At once the pup drove hard, darting along the ridge with her good eye fixed unerringly on the spot where she had seen the sand move. As she drove past the tall forest of weed a grey flash butted her lightly in passing, then swerved to make away at speed along the reef side. Rondo tried to turn quickly, squeaking loudly in fright, a thin trace of bubbles rising from her mouth. She was puzzled and looked around aimlessly for what had streaked by then disappeared. She drifted slowly past the spot where sand still hung, clouding the water, not realising that Rainha had stopped only ten seal's lengths away and was pointing straight towards her. The cow moved a front flipper, fanning the water almost imperceptibly to hold herself tight against the reef. The pup's eye caught some sign and focussed quickly, fastening on the shape of the cow, messages racing through her brain.

It was a game! Fear left her as she sensed fun. She tensed, pulling back her lips in mock ferocity to show pink gums and shining, puppy teeth. With every muscle drawn tight she stalked Rainha, moving slowly forward, stopping every seal's length, her vision fixed hard on her mother and threatening to pounce. The cow stared at Rondo, facing her head on to reduce her profile and quivering, waiting for the tiny beast to make her move. When the pup raced towards her mother like a small, fat cannon shell, Rainha broke at the instant she began to move, speeding to the right in a tight swerve, ringing Rondo with broken water before diving to race along the bottom to hide again. She had moved further this time, but the pup knew now what she was about and took her time, moving to just under the surface from where she could best spy the ground below, searching every part of it for the slightest movement or disturbance, all the time tensed and ready to spring. Again Rainha fanned the water with her limbs to hold position, but as she saw the pup's eye fix on her she did not wait for Rondo to move but charged her, racing upwards and swerving to avoid the pup only at the last moment then porpoising over her, a full seal's length above the surface. Rondo chased her as she dived again, catching up from time to time as Rainha slowed but then having to rise in the water to search again as the cow sped off. For almost an hour they played like this, resting occasionally, and in such a way, the healing, yellow fronds of kelp brushed almost continuously against Rondo's wounds.

When the tide dropped away to leave the kelp fringe exposed on the reef, the cow hauled onto the thickest part of it followed by Rondo who began immediately to feed. The weed was only exposed like this for an hour at the bottom of the tide, and before the water rose again, Rainha led her pup back to Resting Rock.. The exercise had tired her, but the kelp had already begun to take effect. The neck wound still stank, but it looked cleaner and wept only a little. Tomorrow they must go again to the reef, and again, day after day, until the wounds began convincingly to heal and the death stench disappeared.

★   ★   ★

After a few days among the yellow streamers, the savage sears above the pup's left eye hardened as new skin grew, knitting to form a tight, diagonal cross. Pain nipped at her as the socket healed and closed forever, but on her neck the skin around the puncture remained pink and angry, and deep inside the wound infection still fought to keep its grip. But the kelp, the Silver Thread of the seals, together with Rainha's milk, kept the rot at bay. Against the odds, Rondo One-Eye began to thrive.

Gerda, the grey newcomer, was seen more often now by Rondo and her mother, and had even dared to haul out on Resting Rock, though making sure she was a safe distance from Rainha. She made playful greetings, sneezing and shaking her head like a dog. At first Rainha had been suspicious of the grey beast, but one morning when she had returned to Resting Rock after hunting and found the pup absent, Gerda had sensed her disquiet. As Rainha swam off to search for Rondo at the kelp reef, the grey seal toured the margins of Bay of Shelters and found Rondo asleep beside the half eaten carcase of a small Tail Shaker, the first live prey she had ever caught. Following the fish from Resting Rock as though in a game, she had taken it almost by accident while nosing aimlessly among the weed where it had hidden. Feeling flesh between her teeth for the first time, a Message of The Ages had spoken to her and she had brought the little fish quickly to the surface then stripped the flesh of one side from the bone and eaten hungrily. Pleased with herself, she had fallen asleep. When Gerda saw her on the shore she gave a long, eerie wail in her own tongue which woke the pup and was also heard by Rainha as she swam on the far side of Sword Island. Returning, she found Rondo and Gerda playing together close to Resting Rock, and from then, the young, grey cow was no longer looked on as a stranger.

Gerda often followed Rondo and her mother when, perhaps twice a day, they went to the Kelp. The pup was much stronger now, and on her face and around the joints of her limbs the wrinkles had all but disappeared as loose skin became filled by growing muscle and a thickening layer of blubber. She had begun, too, to learn some of the tricks and skills of her Kind as she chased and played. She still fed greedily from Rainha and, at three weeks old, was almost twice as heavy as she had been at birth.

⋆　⋆　⋆

Drought still parched the land and Leaper and Tail Shaker were scarce in the loch. The rains which would allow them to run the rivers to their birth streams had not arrived so they waited outside The Narrows, safer in the wide expanse of Big Firth than in Loch Shiel. In Bay of Shelters, only Rainha, Rondo and Gerda the grey cow remained, all others having moved further down the loch or beyond The Narrows to the flats of Sallachan in search of food.

One morning the seals woke under the first dull sky for many weeks. From a tall crag above the eyrie Talon looked westward, sensing change. She launched, and with her wings tilted to take the breeze, soared high above Dun Mountain and circled to view her ground. She saw Rainha in the water swimming close to Sword Island, and as she looked again to the west, watched wave-building breezes scour Big Firth and begin to funnel through The Narrows to the oaken banks of Loch Shiel. Rising again and calling to her mate, she flew north to hunt, knowing she might have but one chance before the weather changed.

Rainha swam to the kelp bed followed closely by the pup. She held her head high, sniffing the air for signs of travelled, seaborne wind, and hurried Rondo, almost pushing her around the yellow beds. Gerda had not left Bay of Shelters and played alone at the mouth of Rough River, rolling and splashing, holding her head high occasionally like Rainha, her nostrils twitching in growing excitement.

The air became heavy throughout the day until, by late afternoon, angry, rolling clouds were piled like rubble outside The Narrows, and an evil haze glowered above the horizon. Rainha took Rondo to the kelp a second time, but left her to play among the weed, chasing small crabs and flatfish while she herself swam out into the loch and stood on her tail to watch as the clouds darkened slowly and took the red storm-tinge all creatures know. They returned to Resting Rock together and hauled high onto the slab. Along the western coast, fishing boats and yachts scurried for shelter as gale warnings were sounded through the gathering clouds, until for a long while the world seemed to stand still as men and creatures waited silently.

Only Gerda remained in the loch, for the growing, salt-filled wind came to her almost as a mystical embrace which held her there, locked in the water. It came, too, as an image, one of a vast expanse of grey, spume flecked ocean and of long, white-frilled, combing waves built by the wind from rolling swells, seeking out and destroying every weakness as they travelled in fury on the pathway of The Ages. It told of contests; of the richness of victories among the silver shoals below the waves, and the grey cow harkened, seeing again the great gathering places of her Kind on rocky, storm-bitten strands: and she watched, like a man in a far land, loving well that place but loving more his home; dreaming and remembering.

The clouds sat motionless above The Narrows as though waiting for a sign, and then, in the last hour of flood tide, began to flatten out, rolling to each side. It grew darker and cloud and mountain seemed to merge. The west became a fiery orange, then deepest red and purple, changing, minute by minute until, as the ebb began, the high colour was ringed by a sickly, yellow tinge, and every branch sang as the wind began to lift.

As the regiments broke and marched landwards, bird and beast made safe their young. Seals gathered in sheltered places, in small bays and coves and in the lee of small islets and skerries or on narrow ledges overhung by white splashed cliffs. On Resting Rock, Rondo sensed the change and shuffled closer to her mother. At last light the two seals were settled high on their slab. Only Gerda remained in the loch, watching from the crest of every growing wave as the people of the Village moved among flickering lights, securing anything the gale might move, and looking anxiously from their doorways at the tallest of Owl Oaks, some stag-headed, dying and ready to fall in the first, big blow.

The breeze grew stronger, blowing lines of light spray close above the surface. As night fell the sounds of water crashing over rock began to drown those of groaning branches and the hiss of wind in leaves and bushes. By midnight the first rain was falling. Clouds clung to hillsides as they loosed, first, a thin drizzle which was sucked in by the parched earth and then, dense, moving curtains of heavy rain which bounced from the rocks to be spread again as spray by every new gust of wind.

As the ebb tide fought against rising wind, waves became tall and tightly packed, their combing tops blown flat except where the gale was turned by some steep buttress or face of rock, and coils of spindrift were lifted, high above the loch, like whirling, silver dervishes in the blackness of night. The land became sodden and leaves were beaten by the blast until they snapped from brittle, drought-dried branches to be blown far up into the long glen of Rough River. Rondo huddled against her mother as the rain beat down on Resting Rock, where by now Gerda also lay, hauled close to the two others.

After a few hours the wind shifted and began to curl round Sword Island so that a strong draught blew across the backs of the seals. Rainha lifted her head, sniffing, sensing the true direction of the wind before moving, shuffling a few feet higher and bringing herself as far into the lee of Sword Island as she could, murmuring for Rondo to follow. There was north in the gale now, and Rainha knew that with the wind changed to that direction the temperature would fall towards the line where it would be warmer for a seal to be in the water out of the wind-chill rather than lose ever more body heat from the cold blast. But in taking that course there lay another danger, for with the ground unable to absorb so much rain the excess ran off at such speed into streams and rivers, that by the time they reached the loch they had turned brown and muddy, staining Bay of Shelters and turning it into a death trap for a young or weak seal.

★ ★ ★

As dawn forced its will upon a leaden sky, every water-course was full and some had already burst their banks. Water had poured from every hillside into the dry beds, each rising and coursing more and more strongly on their paths towards the lower slopes, tumbling, roaring against rock and bank across a drenched and shining mountain. Branch and blade bowed to the wind, and on Loch Shiel, twigs and leaves blew wildly before being locked for a while in eddying corners, then whirling as the wind shifted a few degrees lifting them from the surface yet again. Foam fringed crests, now with a golden tinge as the gale licked at them through broken sunshine, drove eastward to thunder onto shore and island. Salt spray and rain mingled in curving lines to lash the Village, and men and women looked out in wonder at the storm's fury, think-ing anxiously of things they had left undone.

On Resting Rock, Rondo was in misery. The rain pun-ished the edges of her neck wound and made them raw, heavy drops bruising the soft, unhealed skin, making her whimper and push ever closer to her mother in vain attempts to escape the beating. Rainha turned her head and looked out over Bay of Shelters: the wind was now north-west, chill and dangerous, coursing round each side of Dun Mountain to be funnelled by the hills on either side of the loch until, at Sword Island, it turned and flew in wild abandon over the flood plain of Rough River.

Without warning Gerda splashed noisily into the loch, the wind chill by now too much for her, and Rainha watched as the young cow swam into the bay a dozen lengths then floated upright with only her nose exposed above the waves. Bay of Shelters had remained calm, but out of the lee of Sword Island, grey walls of water crashed, one onto another, as they met the strengthening current of Rough River head on, then fell, foaming, by the battlement that was the shore. The river was already brown, and Rainha watched as the mountain stain spread inexorably into Bay of Shelters, clinging first to the shore then swelling outwards into the loch: she knew her pup was cold, her misery increasing by the minute as heat flowed from her body.

In the high glen at the head of Rough River, small feeder streams and runners scoured green slime from long-stagnant pools and ran now, tumbling into larger burns where soil was torn from the edges piece by piece and boiled in the deeps of pools before pouring like rich ale into the main river. In his dry holt under an old alder, Lutra, the dog otter, heard the rising river sound and curled tighter, tucking nose and head under his rudder-like tail, knowing that should the river rise too far he had a safe escape, and another haven on the hillside above, a safe cairn long deserted by the foxes which had once used it, where he could lie up, dry and deep, sleeping out the storm.

Rainha had no such shelter, for to seal and otter The Ages had shown different paths, and the Kinds of Rainha and Gerda were creatures of open water, taking their chances without the use of holes and cairns. Rondo shivered violently as she tried to keep warm. The cow felt her pup's discomfort and knew that with the wind in this direction she must protect Rondo from the chill. She had already shuffled further to windward to create the best lee she could for the pup, and now pushed Rondo towards the udder. Once fed, the pup dozed, still shivering until she felt the milk begin to warm her belly and welcome heat flowed through her body. It was enough for now.

The people of the Village turned their minds to the day ahead. Rough River had become a torrent, and across its flood plain a muddy, brown pool had formed, swirling through fence and dyke as it sought the lowest ground before joining as one with Loch Shiel. The bridge over the river, which carried the road to the town twelve miles away, was awash, only its stout railings showing above the flood. Villagers came to look at the scene and discuss what they might do, some sighing in resignation, returning home and telephoning to say they would be absent from work that day. Others made light of it and ran the flood, driving hard over the bridge in flying, muddy spray, keeping their engines at full power until they cleared the deepest part of the long, spreading pool. The noise of wind and torrent still screamed in the ears of all things, and man, bird and beast, all that could, kept to the shelter of their homes.

The tide rose rapidly that morning as the power of a wind driven ocean threw its weight against The Narrows, forcing a massive volume of water through the gap. Rainha watched as the level rose and rose, and sensing danger, turned and nosed the pup before sliding into the loch to seek the only shelter that remained. Still drowsy, Rondo followed haltingly and woke fully only as she felt the water cradle her. For a few minutes they remained close to Resting Rock. The loch was the colour of dark ale and the pup, unable to see anything below the surface, clung like a limpet to Rainha's side, grabbing her mother with small, front flippers as they drifted slowly out into Bay of Shelters. The cow murmured continuously in a low voice, reassuring the pup as for the moment she kept almost upright in the water, Rondo's head nuzzling her neck, watching, sensing every sound and movement on the loch and hearing the roar of Rough River grow by the minute until it was even louder than the wind.

Thoughts raced through the cow's brain. She had to find somewhere safe for her pup and knew well that Boat Bay, many seal's lengths across the loch, could be her only choice and that to reach it would be dangerous. To stay here in Bay of Shelters was impossible, for until the rain abated and both Rough River and the tide fell back, they couldn't haul again on Resting Rock. The water of the Bay was by now almost saltless, swollen as it was by so much rain and debris from the hill. It had to be Boat Bay. Rainha turned to face the storm, swimming slowly so the pup could follow.

At the edge of Sword Island they felt the swell which only a few seal's lengths further out into the loch was transformed into grey, high curling waves. Her surface view blocked by the rolling towers and with spray driven continuously into her eyes, Rainha could barely see ahead. She dived through the line of muddy water, signalling Rondo to follow and making directly for the bottom, ten seal's lengths below. Rondo had been more and more frightened by the crashing, broken water of the surface and followed the cow, still fearful but without complaint, her good eye casting about and doing its best to focus on something familiar. The water cleared as they went deeper but it remained dark, the soup above cutting out any light which, normally, would filter almost to the seabed here. The pup tailed Rainha closely, never deviating, her head almost between the cow's sweeping rear limbs. They approached the middle of the loch and she knew she had never been to such a depth. There were flashes of new sights to distract her even in the darkness, but she knew she could not explore, only follow as close to Rainha as she was able. The mother cow looked back often, murmuring reassurance as they crossed the loch's floor. As they came to a field of vast boulders, torn from the hill as the ice had tracked seawards thousands of years ago, Rainha rose a little from the bottom, knowing the place well and sensing the end of their journey. As they neared the north side of the loch the ground began to rise steeply. Banks of rubble, bedecked with weeds and grasses, blocked their path, and Rainha turned and swam west, following a contour and by now only a few seal's lengths below the surface. Rondo heard again the crashing sea above them and looked up in renewed fear, flapping with her rear limbs so that she almost careered past her mother who slowed and calmed her for a few moments. They swam on beneath the maelstrom, breaking the surface fleetingly to draw breath, and after only a few more minutes, Rainha turned again, the pup now level with her as the sounds from above became softer and more distant.

Rainha surfaced slowly, almost lazily, and as Rondo broke from the darkness next to her she saw that they had found calmer water. They were safe under the aspen clad cliffs of the north side of Boat Bay. It was too steep for the seals to haul out on that side so they stayed where they were and floated upright, their heads tilted back slightly and only the tips of their noses above the surface. Rondo stayed close, clinging to the mother cow with her fore limbs as she drifted into sleep.

The ebb began to drag the dark stain seawards from Bay of Shelters. Waves were tinged brown and the sea beneath had filled with the Glen Scent of Rough River and now travelled more and more quickly towards Big Firth and the noses of Leaper and Tail Shaker. By mid-morning the rain had slackened. The wind dropped and veered again into the south, but still the seals remained under their cliff waiting for the tide to fall further and for Bay of Shelters to clear of the debris which by now was everywhere and gathered into large, sodden clumps.

A few birds began to move around, and on Dun Mountain, Talon's Eaglet, now full-feathered, stood wet and hungry at the edge of the ancient eyrie, shaking and calling for food. Far above on their resting ledges, Talon and Chryso heard the young bird's cries but did not stir. The eaglet must fly of its own accord, and in the way of The Ages, until she had taken her first, clumsy flight, the parent birds would provide her with no more food at the eyrie. But they had dropped the carcase of a mountain hare within her sight a few hundred feet below the nest, and knew that hunger would soon drive her to it from the sodden basket. After she had made that first flight Talon and Chryso would begin to teach her to hunt for herself, and just as the

Northland's seals had learned to bear their pups at a time when food was plentiful, so, too, had learned the Kind of Talon, for there were young grouse on Dun Mountain now, and the calves of red deer, some of which would become weak or lame. All these things were in the eaglet's larder, and like Rondo One-Eye, only provided she learned quickly would she come to feed herself and flourish.

Chryso soared eastwards from his ledge as glimpses of sun began to break above the wet, shining slopes of his domain. Continuous rain had turned to long showers, and between these he saw a steely glint come over the loch. From high above, he watched the stain from Rough River spread westward, saw leaf and branch afloat on Loch Shiel and even whole trees. He flew on towards the Village, his eye sharpening to the courses of larger and more powerful streams where a beast might be most likely to drown, overcome by the speed of the flood, but there was nothing. He would not venture beyond the mouth of Rough River for that was the territory of another eagle, a sister of Talon's, and as he wheeled above the enlaked flood plain and turned again for Dun Mountain, he saw two seals lying on the shore on the east side of Boat Bay.

Rondo had fed in the water as Rainha floated on her back to make it easier for the hungry pup, but much of the milk had been spilled. The cow looked across the bay to where a small shack stood between Owl Oaks and the shore. It was a sheltered place, but being so close to men was seldom used by any seal. The oaks still swayed noisily in the wind, but there was no sign of life, no other noise nor any human voice. Rainha swam to the middle of the bay with the pup riding on her back, clinging to her neck. As she touched the gravel beach below the shack she tipped the youngster off and hauled a short way above the falling tideline. There, Rondo fed once more, and as the warmth of milk flooded her and she began to doze, she saw a small, black dot above her in the sky.

Rainha looked at the pup as she slept. The eye had almost completely healed into the fallen cross which was to distinguish Rondo all of her life, but the neck wound was still pink

and raw, though it remained closed and had lost the angry
swelling that had surrounded it for many weeks. The kelp
had done its work; but now Rainha knew there was another
hurdle, and within another week the pup's wounds must be
completely healed so she could be put among the Leapers
which would arrive now, following the Glen Scent which had
been carried seaward by the storm. Like Talon's Eaglet,
Rondo had reached the age when she must learn to hunt.

Chapter 8

Over the next few days the level of Rough River fell slowly until at last it settled, its colour changing slowly from dark ale to gold. The flood plain reappeared, greener now, and with a freshness not seen for many months. New sounds were heard in Bay of Shelters, and from Resting Rock, Rondo heard for the first time the splashing of Leaper and Tail Shaker as they gathered eagerly around the river mouth. The next spate would allow them to run the length of Rough River to their birth streams, but for now they came and went with the tide, some swimming through the river's tidal pools on the high flood until, unable to surmount the falls above the bridge for lack of water, they returned to the loch and sought the ancient lodges of their Kind, waiting fitfully for more rain.

Rondo's wound healed steadily as Rainha continued to take her to the reef. She grew stronger, heavier, and the two seals ranged further, swimming past the smooth rock men called the Whaleback and going west towards Birthing Rock, playing and hauling in small bays and on tight, silver beaches. Occasionally, Eye-Peckers landed close to the seals as they lay dozing, but Rondo's fear of the birds had turned to hatred and it was always she who rose, snarling to the attack as Rainha looked on. More seals gathered in the loch, following the ever increasing shoals of Leapers from The Narrows, but Rondo, though curious, was unused to company and stayed apart from all but her mother and Gerda. She still dozed after each feed and was no longer afraid to wake and find her mother gone. Rainha hunted hard, filling her belly with the pink flesh of salmon, fattening herself after the drain of keeping Rondo in milk, and knowing that, at least until the next new moon she must continue to nourish the pup to give her the best chance of surviving through her first winter.

It was a time of plenty. Leaper and Tail Shaker arrived in greater numbers with each flood tide, their long journeys almost complete. They had travelled from the krill-rich deeps of the Greenland sea and beyond, high above the winter ice lines of the far north. Now they returned, each beckoned by a Message of The Ages to seek its own Glen Scent and return to the stream of its birth to repeat the ancient cycle in the life of its Kind.

In strengthening, Rondo began to grow supple. As is the way with all creatures, she grew more and more curious of her surroundings and all that lived there. She did not hunt seriously, as Rainha's milk still surged in her, but as her independence grew the pup was left alone more often by the mother cow and began to catch small fish and eels in Bay of Shelters and around the kelp beds she had come to know so well. The neck wound had healed, and her coat began to grow around the weal so that soon only the cross over her left eye would bear witness to her early sufferings. Over half her days and nights were spent in sleep, but through her waking hours the lessons of The Ages were being learned in earnest. Because of the effects of her wounds she was slightly smaller than others her own age. She had learned early the effects of pain and fear, but now she learned constructively of deeps and shallows, of how to find the lodges of their creatures and how to stalk, when to strike or whether to kill by stealth or speed, as all her Kind had done since the days of The Seal Fathers. But for Rondo, all these things were being learned without the benefit of two eyes.

Some things had come naturally, like using her whiskers to probe for movement among the weeds; or digging with her nose along a muddy bottom to frighten large, pink prawns from their burrows. But hard work for such small returns would never bring her to full size and, like Talon's eaglet, the skills she needed to progress to adulthood would not be found until the cutting urgency of hunger honed her mind. Crabs, small eels and flatfish began more and more to replace Rainha's milk. Apart from the small Tail Shaker she had already caught by accident, their larger cousins, though now plentiful, had so far eluded her, for she had not yet attained the speed or guile required to take them without tiring herself beyond the value of the effort.

At five weeks old Rondo's wounds had ceased to bother her and were all but forgotten. Though the memory of the Eye-Peckers would stay with her forever, she felt no real loss in having only one eye, since she had known nothing else. Her head was held almost permanently a little to the left, and her right eye had grown strong and quick to compensate the loss of the other. Pain had hardened her and she strove hard, learning, perhaps, more quickly than her peers, so that she flourished with new knowledge.

Rainha's milk yield began naturally to decrease, for she had by now begun to feel a different Message, one which had come to her at this time each year since before the birth of her first, doomed pup eight years before. Soon, when the call came, she would find her bull and mate with him among the sea wrack of South Shore, obeying The Ages as her Kind had done since before the days of The Seal Fathers. But for a few days yet she still played fondly with her pup, keeping her active and taking her to far places, showing her the lodges of cod and conger, and sand beds where plaice and sole lay hidden, flattened to the bottom. She brought Rondo to The Narrows as the ebb tide tore between its cliffs, so she might feel the sea's grip, its mighty power, and learn to use it. They made on to Sallachan that day and hauled high on the shore, and from that place, Rondo One-Eye first viewed the world that lay beyond Loch Shiel.

One evening, as a gentle breeze dropped to leave the loch calm, and a round, red sun dipped behind Dun Mountain, the two seals returned to Resting Rock and hauled onto the warm granite. Just after midnight there was the slightest splash as a beast slid into the water and swam around the north side of Sword Island. There, the seal paused, looking back before making off towards The Narrows. An hour later, Rainha was close to Birthing Rock, looking out across the dark glass, waiting for some unseen companion.

On Resting Rock, Rondo still slept. The call had come to her mother as surely as it had done to every cow for all the time of their Kind, and for her pup, from this time, nothing would ever be the same again. In a week or two Rainha would return but would be different, more detached. Rondo would no longer be able to demand her attention, and though she might follow the cow and hunt with her it would no longer be as of right, but as a respectful novice, tolerated and encouraged so long as she held to the rules and kept her place in the complex society of which they were both part.

*   *   *

Two mornings later, in Bay of Shelters, Gerda whistled as she saw Rondo waken and shuffle round to view the loch. Still yawning, the pup greeted her then slid into the water, splashing and rolling on her back under the early sun. Fully awake, she swam to the edge of the bay to where she could spy the length of Loch Shiel, thinking there might be some sign of Rainha. She lifted her head as high as she could above the ripples, focussing her good eye on the middle distance, but saw nothing, so dived and searched lazily below for a few minutes. This was the longest period Rainha had ever remained absent, but by now the pup was almost able to maintain her weight without milk. Without the need for that sustenance the tie between mother and daughter was already loosening, and she was not over troubled by her mother's absence, for she had already sensed change and perhaps saw this new event as just another in a succession of happenings, part of the rapid process of learning which had been the major part of her short life. She swam back to the bay and sought out her grey friend.

Gerda, too, had sensed something. A few days before she had been at Birthing Rock and watched as the bulls gathered among the other beasts; cows with pups, the immature and elderly. Although they were not of her own Kind, Gerda knew by The Ages of the ancient ritual that was about to take place, and had dreamed again of her own birthplace, seeing, through the Eye of The Ages, the long, grey beaches

crowded with hundreds of seals and echoing to the bellowing of bulls. The animals of Rainha's kind made little noise
compared to those of her own, but there were slighter
sounds, and there were postures, games and smells, all of
which woke in Gerda instincts and senses born of The Ages
and which lived in every beast and bird. In a few years these
senses would flower in her and she, too, would return to the
far, storm-lashed strand of her dreams to mate.

Such things were not much in her mind as she played with
Rondo around the slabs at the mouth of Rough River. She
caught a large flatfish and splashed with it in the shallows,
tossing the fish high in the air then chasing as it tried weakly
to escape. Rondo dashed around the grey beast, feinting in
mock attack and trying playfully to steal the fish, but Gerda
could not be fooled, and ignoring the pup, began to eat.
Lying afloat on her back, holding the fish to her chest with
supple, fore limbs, she stripped flesh from bone, eating until
she satisfied her hunger and the bony skeleton was discarded
to drop among the crabs and other creatures of the loch
bottom. Rondo began to hunt as Gerda swam towards
Resting Rock to haul out and relax after her feed. She sniffed
at the remains of the grey's meal, nibbling at it to see if anything was left, but its bareness served only to lift her hunger
and her attention became focussed, concentrated on the
search for food. The pup gathered what she could, nosing
prawns from the mud and raiding mussel beds which lay
along the shore for the small, green crabs that made their
lodges there. She crushed them between her jaws, sucking
out the meat and spitting grit and shell back into the water.

Recently, among the tangled weeds she had begun more
and more to chance upon the dens of small saithe and cod
and learned quickly to hunt them as she had done with
Rainha during their games among the kelp, hanging motionless and holding her head to the left to give her good eye
fullest scope, waiting for the slightest movement. She missed
often, but as her attention span lengthened she came to
know that catching food was not an easy matter and required
skill and concentration. In this way she learned patience and
began to take more and more time in the stalk, edging a little

at a time towards whatever blur of bottom sand or shake of weed had caught her eye. She began to enjoy her hunting more, sometimes even teasing fish as they fled, until at last she would drive hard, flushing from weed and crevice with sharp, twisting turns to catch a hapless fish across the back, nipping life from it almost at first touch. With these new skills, speed and an easy grace grew quickly in her, and though she could not rival Gerda's slim, graceful elegance below the waves, her confidence grew daily and she moved steadily towards a point where, provided there was food about, she could fill her belly in a fairly short time.

Now, the recent sight Gerda's catch had made her even hungrier. Diving to the loch floor she scoured the area around the mouth of Rough River where, usually, all manner of fish could be found. She nosed around, using her whiskers to search the smallest cracks, feeling for the slightest movement that would give away the presence of a fish. She stalked each bank of weed, noting the current so that she followed it, where possible, upstream; the way in which her quarry would be pointing. Rondo tried to search, too, in a clockwise manner, for in this way she gave her good, right eye full scope ahead, and by making a slow, full roll every so often, could see outwards, below and above.

Well out in the loch, in a direct line from the river mouth, were several large boulders, dumped there by the ice, now weed-strewn and half covered with the silt washed from Rough River's glen. Rondo approached with care, skirting them by thirty seal's lengths until she was the same distance down current, then, staying slightly to the left of the boulders, turning to face back towards the river. She sank slowly to the bottom, staying only far enough above the silt to ensure she made no clouds as her limbs moved gently to hold position. She had hunted around this place before, though never on her own. Long tendrils of kelp and bladder wrack reached upwards from their anchor points on the rocks, all bent slightly towards her in the current, their fronds spread out as they reached full height: it was a sea forest, hiding all manner of things in its shade. The seal crept on towards the boulders. Light from above flickered among the weed so that the view was ever changing, always moving; confusing the young hunter but helping to hide among its dappled strands, anything that feared it would be hunted. Rondo stopped and hung in the water. As her limbs moved to hold her still they worked so slowly that it appeared to be the current that moved them and not the animal herself. It was as though she had become part of the loch bottom, a weed-covered rock or an old, silted-over tree, rounded, the broken stumps of its branches almost completely hidden. Her eye was focussed perfectly but she could see nothing move. Still she remained there, treading time with every system of her body slowed to the bare minimum, the air in her lungs drip-feeding oxygen to her bloodstream which now merely trickled through her veins, all in the Way of The Ages.

Where she lay hidden, to a fish she was indistinguishable from the debris of the loch floor. Her eye moved to a barely discernible glimmer among the weed beyond the nearest boulder, and slowly, she began to drift forward to within ten seal's lengths of the movement, her eye fastened to the exact place she had first seen it, her mind sifting through all she had ever learned, removing all unnecessary information so that what worked in her head was only what could assess what the movement might be and what she must do to capture it with the least effort. The Ages spoke to her of patience and she drifted again, even more slowly now, towards the weeds. A small cloud passed across the sun, and for a moment the confused flickering stopped and allowed her a clear view.

It was enough, for she had seen the long, deep shape clearly and was tensed already, every sense keening to the hunt that must now follow. The Ages spoke again and she drifted a little more, then more, until, half hidden from the creature by the nearest rock she was almost perfectly placed to complete the stalk. Drifting to her left she straightened, her body tight, every nerve and muscle ready to drive. Rondo did not know what her quarry was for she had not yet learned to recognise each Kind by where it was to be found, the way it hunted or swam, or what type of weed or crevice it preferred

as a hiding place. A little closer now and she could see for
the first time the straight, trailing edge of a thick, dark tail.
Still, it had not seen her. Her forward movement had become continuous but so slow as to be barely perceptible. She
rose a little in the water so that when she struck it would be
from slightly above the fish, and just as Talon the she eagle
would take a mountain hare, the advantage of height would
allow her to accommodate almost any sideward move the
fish might make.

As she came to within four seal's lengths and inclined
slightly downwards towards the fish there was the slightest
movement ahead of her and she glimpsed for the first time
the unmistakable flash of silver which, together with the
straight edge of its tail could mean but one thing. It was a
Tail Shaker; a mighty fish weighing as much as Rondo
herself had weighed at birth: a blue and silver arrow of raw,
powerful muscle, fresh from the feeding grounds of
Greenland, and one which, in the course of its three years of
life since leaving the Glen of Rough River, had already
escaped attacks by seals from The Narrows to the Arctic Sea.
Young Rondo could not have the slightest chance.

The fish was almost hard against a rock to its right and
hidden by thick fronds of sea wrack. It could only break left
or straight ahead. She needed more height but dare not risk
the smallest movement, for the fish might move again soon
and this time would surely see her. The time for patience
was past; the stalk was over and she must move within the
next few seconds or lose her meal. She would need to surface
for air in less than a minute. The Ages spoke: her limbs were
ready. She drove on.

Speeding forward she flicked her front, left flipper outwards for a split second, using it to alter both height and
direction. She had been right, for silver flashed in her eye as
the fish broke left, its wedge shaped tail powering it away.
She had moved above and to the left of the fish as she began
her drive and was now able to travel in a straight line as the
Tail Shaker arced outwards from the rock and its blanket of
weed. She closed her jaws too soon, and as the creature felt
teeth close around its tail it panicked and drove even harder,

twisting and weaving in its flight as the thin, outer membrane of its tail tore slightly. With a burst of extra power it raced almost directly upwards, leaving Rondo below, confused and with not even a few scales around her mouth to show for her work.

The Tail Shaker sped on towards Boat Bay, now close to the surface, frightened, still panicking and with no plan except to swim as fast and far from the seal as it could. Rondo searched for the fish using all her speed, rolling, scouring all the boulders in the field from above, dashing in if she suspected movement, always anxious to keep the initiative and give the Tail Shaker as little advantage as possible. Seeing nothing she swam to the surface to breathe then dived again quickly.

The fish had broken left from its hiding place. Rondo had already searched the boulder field and knew that if not hidden there it may have held its ultimate direction and swum south-west. Keeping about five seal's lengths from the loch bottom and rolling right round every few seconds she made off at speed towards Boat Bay. As she approached the rock which marked the entrance she porpoised noisily, repeating the action twice more as she rounded the point and entered the bay, knowing the noise would warn the fish that she was following, keeping panic in its brain, tiring it and increasing her chances of success. The stalk had been successful; only her ability to strike accurately had let her down. She had about four minutes before she used more energy than the fish could return to her if captured and eaten. She swung round, following the line of gravel beach, more slowly now and still rolling so her single eye was given every chance to cover everything. There was a disused slipway in shallow water at the end of the beach where old ropes and wires were rotting slowly about a seal's length below the surface. They were encrusted with mussels and limpets and strewn with weed to form a dense, confusing mass in which the light played tricks of blurring and glinting. The seal stopped. She remembered this place, dark and bright all at once, where it had always been difficult for her eye to cope with the confused light. Something told her to go in. She knew her way through the tangled mess and would be in no danger from anything.

The Tail Shaker had heard her round the point and raced immediately for cover; any cover, and there, among man's debris, had thought it had found safety. Rondo moved in slowly, cautious of her movements and checking from above every exit from the tangle that a fish might use. She could see nothing to point to a fish being there and circled, breaking the surface and almost touching the shore. A few small fish, each less than a mouthful, flitted among the weeds close to the bottom, but otherwise, nothing stirred. She moved away a few lengths, pushing herself backwards with her front flippers and keeping her eye always on the hideout, scanning for the slightest puff of mud or any strange movement among the weed.

A young codling no longer than a seal's whisker swam aimlessly just outside the edge of the tangle. Rondo watched as it turned and headed inward towards a loop of thick wire that hung from the old slipway rails where they jutted from the shore. The wire was almost covered with bladder wrack and sea grass, and an empty, rusty oil drum lay on its side beneath, so that the whole, confused mess had become something like a marine burrow. The codling hesitated outside the entrance then moved in again and disappeared from Rondo's view. Then, like a dart the fish shot from the hole and raced out across the loch floor, lost from sight almost as soon as it had appeared. Rondo needed no further sign. Rising a seal's length she moved ahead until above the entrance to the burrow. She rolled on her back and looked down. She could see nothing but knew that this was not a time for stealth. There was no other cover nearby. The fish would know of her presence and already be severely frightened; she had to make it panic completely yet still keep control. She allowed herself to drift to the surface, still on her back and with her eye fixed on the burrow mouth, her long whiskers feeling for any swirl from below. She moved her fore limbs steadily, holding position but causing stirs and currents to eddy round the tangle, letting the Tail Shaker know she was there, every move designed to frighten the fish and bring closer the point where it became convinced it had no option but to flee. She blew into the water and a stream of bubbles shot downwards. As they began to drift slowly back to the surface, they were suddenly atomised by a flash of silver.

Rondo felt the fish move before it seared through the entrance, and sensing the first driving swing of its great tail she had twisted, slapping the surface with her rear limbs to induce more panic while turning on her belly and driving into the chase. Half a seal's length behind, she followed not only by eye but with every sense of The Ages, feeling the swirl of the fish's wake on her whiskers, hearing the beating of the wedged tail and seeing that glimmering of blue and silver, swerving now, twisting and darting as panic gripped ever harder at the Tail Shaker's mind. But still, it was not enough, for the ultimate error must be made before the seal could strike and she alone could bring about that final, fatal mistake. Down she went, underneath the fish so it could no longer see her without moving its head away from the track of its escape, diverting its attention, slowing it down and leaving it no choice but to race upwards from the unseen enemy, hoping to confuse the seal by clearing the surface in a great leap, and then, as the hunter closed and made to strike, falling back and diving deep and fast to leave Rondo near the surface without sight or sound of it. But The Ages held the pup and she almost stopped, waiting a length below the surface as the fish leapt. It cleared three of its own lengths, its wedge tail shaking violently as it fell back, already driving for the bottom, fifty seal's lengths below.

Rondo had thought her work almost done as the fish leapt, but now was forced to move more quickly than she had ever done before. Such was the Tail Shaker's speed, even as it hit the surface, that she was taken completely by surprise. She twisted cleverly, and was blessed with enough luck to find herself in the fish's path. The Tail Shaker made a wild and brave attempt to jink but Rondo's jaws, already closing on its back, fell firm and fast, shaking the silver giant to break its spine and work the life from it. The pup broke surface and drew breath, then, triumphantly, as the Tail Shaker flapped its

last between her jaws she threw it high in the air, not bother-
ing to retrieve her prize for several seconds after it had landed.

Twenty minutes later she was on Resting Rock. Gerda had
watched as Rondo struggled up the slab. The Tail Shaker
was a giant of its Kind, so large that the pup's jaws could not
contain it fully, and once out of the water her young muscles
were not even strong enough to support its weight. She half
dragged, half carried the fish as high as she could go without
exhausting herself, then turned her back to the grey cow and
growled a little before she began to eat. She had taken a few
bites while still in the water, but was not yet big enough to
eat such a creature lying on her back and holding it steady
with her fore limbs. The only answer had been Resting Rock
where she risked having her catch stolen by older, larger
seals, but once again luck had been with her, for there were
no others on the slab but Gerda who had only recently eaten
and was unlikely to be a threat.

The hunt had been the longest and most intense of her life
so far and she ate gratefully, already tired and needing rest.
The fish was a quarter of her own weight and there was no
way in which she could eat all of it at once. Nonetheless, she
made a determined effort and was soon belching loudly as
her belly filled almost to bursting point. When she could eat
no more she had to struggle in order to shuffle round to look
out across the bay. Her eye kept closing and her head
nodded then pulled up with a start as she realised she was
falling asleep. She could not hold herself awake no matter
how she tried and within a few minutes was in a deep, full-
bellied sleep.

⋆   ⋆   ⋆

It was August and the long days of summer had begun to
shorten. The parched look of the countryside had disappeared as showers were fed regularly onto the coast by
southerly winds, and every branch was lush with the heavy
greenery of full summer. Hillsides turned blue as heather
blossomed and there was a richness of life over all the land
and in the waters of the coast.

Rainha had returned after an absence of almost two weeks. She had mated with Vitula, Rondo's father, and now carried the seed of new life which would lie in her until it grew and was brought forth next midsummer. At first the cow was distant and ignored the pup's welcoming and en-quiring squeaks and whistles, but after a few days they began to swim and haul out together once again, and with Gerda the grey cow, took their ease in the waters of Bay of Shelters and on the warm slab of Resting Rock.

For many birds and beasts it was a time of plenty, a time to fatten before the cold, hard months of shortened daylight and the loss of plentiful food and warmth. In Bay of Shelters the seals hunted during the few hours before and after high and low tides when Leaper and Tail Shaker became agitated and ignored danger, swimming close to the mouth of Rough River. Rondo still followed her mother whenever she could, growing in strength and skill and always copying Rainha's well tried tactics. In spite of her small size and lack of full sight her success increased steadily, perhaps because she was forced to strive so much harder. Now, as she hunted she would roll every few seconds, and she stopped still in the water more often than did her peers, sensing movement with her long, sensitive whiskers and learning to know the differ-ence between tide swirl and the side-treading of fish as they lay in hidden in their lodges.

Rainha encouraged the pup's increasing independence almost in a negative way. She no longer looked back every few minutes to ensure Rondo was following, and when she hunted it was to fill her own belly so she more or less ignored the youngster, intent only on rebuilding her blubber layer, still depleted by having had to produce so much milk. It was the way of The Ages. Rondo must be able to feed herself over the coming winter and if she failed in this there was nothing Rainha could or would do to assist her. That purpose would not be well served by a mother cow being attentive so late in the year, but despite these things the bond between the two remained, and the cow still allowed Rondo to haul close to her whenever the pup sought comfort.

Throughout September the seals fed well until, at the very

end of that month, they felt the chill as first the wind died, then turned and came again, rain filled, from the north west. On the heights of Dun Mountain, snow fell during length- ening nights, then melted slowly through the day and ran glistening in a thousand silver streams into Loch Shiel. Leaper and Tail Shaker ran swiftly through the tidal pools of Rough River and hurled themselves ever onwards through cascading waterfalls towards the upper reaches and their birth pools.

As the snow fell, Talon and Chryso sat motionless through the lengthening nights on their resting ledges, their golden heads hidden between the warming feathers of their breasts and the broad quills of their wings. They heard the first roaring of stags in the corries below and knew by The Ages of the time to come; that from now they must be ready to hunt away, far beyond the closest ridges of their home ground until the winter grew late and was at its hardest, and when the weakest of deer and other beasts and birds would begin to succumb to the effects of wind and wet and become easy to kill.

When the roaring of stags was at full pitch and the largest of them fought for mastery over each group of hinds, far away from there another gathering had begun. Many miles to the west, beyond the Isles of Lorne, and past the windswept beaches of the western coast, on rocky, barren islets another roaring was soon to begin. High above the tide lines, the grey cows of Gerda's Kind were gathered, first to give birth to their pups and then, after a few weeks, to mate. Bulls, too, were gathered there, heavy, powerful beasts, each trumpeting his might out over the surf, proclaiming his name and all the names of his line since the days of Halichus, The Seal Father of their Kind. The Messages they gave grew strong in all the cows, and through the Eye of The Ages all knew where to gather, visions and messages guiding them from far out in the ocean.

Rainha had watched as her pup spent more time away from Bay of Shelters. She was fat, fit and well able to look after herself now. One morning as the sun struggled to rise through a streaked October sky, Rainha woke to find no sign of Gerda or pup. The grey cow had grown restless, and as she hunted Leaper or played in Bay of Shelters was distracted easily, often stopping still and holding her head high above the water, looking westwards as though listening for some ancient call. As the last of the season's Leapers ran into Rough River the grey cow moved gradually further down the loch, edging closer to The Narrows and the source of that strange, unheard call which made her all the time more restless and detatched. Rondo, eager for any new experience, had followed her out. She was never to see her mother again.

Chapter 9

The high colour of late autumn was all around as the two seals passed through the tiderace of The Narrows. Steep hillsides were rich with the brown of dead bracken, and birches, now bare of leaves, were painted as groups of pinkish-grey sticks against every slope. There was water in the burns; silver water, gurgling to the sea with purpose in their flow, washing the dead leaves and spent summer petals into Big Firth.

They hauled out at Sallachan among a number of other beasts, all of Rondo's Kind, but the grey cow was fitful and unsettled. The Message of The Ages seemed to rise more in her with every new tide and she knew that soon she would leave this place and travel far. Rondo sensed none of this and busied herself exploring the unfamiliar hunting grounds to ensure she could find food. Two nights after their arrival, Gerda slipped quietly into Big Firth and swam westwards, unnoticed in her leaving even by the one-eyed pup. The Ages had been satisfied, and Rondo One-Eye was on her own.

Some miles from those muddy banks, close to the most westerly of the Islands of Lorne, two fishermen worked nets and pots between the rocks and islets which formed a barrier between the open ocean and Big Firth. Their fathers, too, had been fishermen and they were strong men, well used to the ways of the sea. Born to endure wind and wave, they knew the ways of birds and seals and could read the signs those creatures gave which told of shoals of fish.

In the long nights of winter, when darkness fell at four and the Northlands were without daylight until nine the next

morning, they mended their nets and rested beside fires of
driftwood won from white, Atlantic beaches. There was
music in their souls and many were their tales of eagles and
seals, for their forbears had believed the seals were spirits of
drowned fishermen, returned to watch over families and kin,
and all of them remembered the tale of Harvester and the
Silver Thread.

The end of autumn was a time for catching and salting
down the herring they used as bait in their prawn and lobster
pots throughout the winter. In days past, great shoals of
these fish had visited the western coast every year, coming
close inshore, into every bay and cove so that many men and
boats were needed to haul the long drift nets, so heavy would
they become with silver fish. Now, the two fishers worked
from dawn, watching and waiting until they saw the shoals
flood into a bay or inlet to where they followed them and
shot away their nets. After each good haul they made for
shore, for the boat they used was small and filled quickly.
They ran her onto a sheltered beach below their dwellings
and put the herring into boxes which they covered and
carried high above the tide's reach.

When there were seals around they would clear them by
waving their arms and shouting loudly, for a seal could do
terrible damage, not only by driving fish away in panic from
the natural trap of the bay into the safety of open water, but
should a seal become entangled it would tear a net to pieces
in its struggle to escape and almost certainly drown as it did.
In the boat the fishermen carried a rifle for it was easier and
kinder to shoot a seal gripped in a strong net than try to cut
it free, risking their boat and their own lives only for the seal
to drown or die from the injuries of its struggle.

★   ★   ★

Rondo had wakened before dawn knowing nothing of
Gerda's departure from Sallachan. She yawned, then
stretched to waken her still drowsy muscles, and scratched
herself with each front flipper. It was calm. High above her
on the hill two stags were roaring, their deep bellowing

splitting the silence of darkness and carrying far across Big Firth. The tide was flooding quickly and Rondo glanced at its progress as she looked around the long mudbank at the few other seals hauled out there. She could not see Gerda. Feeling hunger she took to the water.

Swimming slowly on the surface she moved into Big Firth. Everything here was new to her so she took her time, sniffing the air and glancing below the surface every few seconds to watch what lay below. There was a strong tug to the tide as she made directly across its course, and here, too, was the long, low swell seldom felt inside The Narrows. Here in Big Firth a seal must come to know the ocean's movements and Rondo took to it without a second thought.

The one-eyed pup thought she heard Gerda's call as she stopped at daybreak half way across, floating upright so she could turn and swivel, seeing everything that lay around her. The sound seemed to have come from the west and she looked hard, her ears wide in the stillness and her eye keening for a sign of other beasts. There was nothing there. All she could see were the Isles picked out against the low horizon where the Firth left the land forever and became the ocean. The Island shapes beckoned. The pup spun to look back towards The Narrows and stared hard at the outline of Dun Mountain, pencilled against the sky in growing light, and then, with no more hesitation, turned again and swam off steadily towards the Isles of Lorne, knowing nothing of what lay in store for her.

In Loch Shiel, Rainha swam near Bay of Otters, hunting casually. Freed from the responsibility of her pup she had already begun to settle into a routine, working the tides and taking advantage of the sunshine to haul out and relax in the last few weeks before the weather hardened. The slopes of Dun Mountain turned rich red as the morning sun climbed, and were scarred with the clean grey of bare rock and filigreed with slim, silver streams. She thought little of Rondo, for now there was new life in her; still dormant, waiting until the year had turned before it began to grow. But Rainha's new pup was not to know a life; never to watch in childish fear as Talon crossed low over the loch, and never to play below the summer sun on the slabs at Rough River's mouth. For the hand of man had forgotten the Message of The Ages. A grim time was to come to the seals; a time of ravaging and destruction seldom seen in all the days since The Seal Fathers.

*   *   *

Rondo approached a group of small, rocky islets, their low crests strewn with patches of coarse, green grass. She skirted them, watching and listening, taking in her new surroundings and staying close to open water in case she might be forced to make a quick escape. Big Firth had scarcely shown a ripple throughout the day, and even the low swell had fallen to the merest rise and fall as the ocean enjoyed a rare period of autumn calm. The silence was broken only by the sounds of a raft of Eider duck which swam nervously ahead of the pup, forming a tight group and quickening away led by a dark, old female as Rondo came too close to them. The seal watched as they moved across the red glare of the sun's passing. She needed a place to haul out in safety and moved inwards, closer to the broken shoreline.

Some miles away the two fishermen moored their boat in the bay and rowed ashore in a small dinghy, discussing the day's work. Once on the beach they carried the boxes of herring over the rise towards their houses, and before going in to eat and warm themselves, salted down their day's catch into large, blue plastic barrels. Earlier, a seal had strayed towards them as they shot their nets. They had shouted and waved their arms to no avail, and undeterred, the beast had come slowly towards them, swimming blindly, straight for the net. They hauled quickly, thinking they might avoid entangling the beast, but puzzled as to why it ignored their warning shouts. They got the net on board as fast as they could, shouting and yelling all the time, but still, the seal refused to turn or dive. The boat was swung round and pointed towards it, usually a sure way of seeing off a bird or beast, but there was no reaction. With the rifle ready by the gunwale they grew closer, realising by now the seal must be sick, but hesitating until they could get close enough for a killing shot and hoping to see what ailed the animal.

As they came within ten seal's lengths they saw how sick it was. The beast's nose and mouth were covered with grey and yellow slime and its eyes were swollen, misted and unseeing. They said nothing, but shook their heads in pity as the beast looked blindly towards them almost as though begging them to end its misery. The shot rang out across Big Firth and the fishers heard the heavy bullet smack into the seal's head. Its eyes closed as though in peace and it rolled over, sinking without haste towards the bottom. It was a shot Rondo had heard but which had not deterred her from her journey. As dusk fell she swam into the bay, hauling onto a narrow beach where an hour earlier, another, diseased and dying seal had been helped there by the rising tide.

Rondo had waited until she felt the tide slacken. She was tired and needed rest but there was a strange smell around and she was not sure of the place she was in. She could have slept at sea, floating upright with only her nose out of the water but she was unsure of the tides. For an hour she waited in the bay, watching until the tide dropped a few lengths from the high water mark before hauling onto the shingle. She dozed, taking her rest though still alert to any noise or disturbance. She had eaten little that day and what she had caught was mainly through luck as she knew nothing of the hunting grounds where she now found herself. If she were to remain here she would have to explore and learn if she was to survive the winter, for only in such a way might she come to learn the best places to feed and the safest in which to shelter from gales or crushing waves.

Hours later the pup was wakened by the noise of an engine, and even before being fully awake had sped across the shingle and into the water, diving to the bottom of the bay and swimming to the middle before surfacing to look back towards the beach. She saw nothing to worry her, but the noise of the engine which had roused her was still loud, carrying far across the water in the still air. She was puzzled. She could see no boats apart from the fishermen's which hung lifeless on its mooring in the bay, and the upturned dinghy, high and dry above the beach. The noise faded quickly but the seal remained where she was, floating vertically in the water, swivelling to give her good eye the broadest view.

She began to swim round, still looking hard. The day had yet to break and though she had seen nothing yet that troubled her, that same odour she had smelled last evening came to her nose once again. It puzzled her, for though she could not recognize it, it was in some strange way familiar and she looked around nervously searching for its source. As she grew close to the shore the smell grew stronger and she shuffled forward in the shallows, her nose and head stretched out as she peered across the shingle. Still, she saw nothing; but curiosity held her and she continued moving, half swimming in the shallows along the shoreline. Almost at the end of the shingle was a large, half-buried boulder. Rondo approached it cautiously and, as she peered round its far side, froze. Lying on its back, mouth and jaws agape and with its eyes horribly swollen lay a large, dead seal.

Chapter 10

The two fishermen had left early that day for market with all the crab and lobster they had caught over the last few weeks. It had been the engine of their truck that had wakened Rondo and sent her fleeing to the water. Well before daybreak they had emptied the keep cages where they held their catch and which were moored in another small bay on the far side of the island. The catch, all still alive, was stacked in boxes onto the pickup, and the men left to go aboard the small ferry which would take them to the mainland.

The load was covered with a dampened, old carpet to keep it hidden from prying eyes, and so it would remain fresh for the French and Spanish buyers who waited in the harbour town some miles away. As the short distance to the mainland was crossed, the fishermen had watched a small group of seals on a rough skerry a hundred seal's lengths from the boat. They talked again of the beast they had been forced to shoot the previous day, and wondered why it had been diseased and in far worse condition than any they had seen before.

In a large lorry park in the town they sold their catch to their regular, French buyer who drove there every week to collect the abundant shellfish of the Northlands. There were many fishermen there, all selling, and after the business of the day they gathered in a bar at the pierhead to talk of prices and weather, of who had bought a new boat or who's banker was being awkward. A few, those who spent the months of summer fishing with bag nets for Leaper and Tail Shaker, began to talk of seals and the terrible damage they had caused to their nets that year, allowing them only the poorest of catches. "Time for a cull." said one, and the others agreed.

The whisky flowed, and in due course one of the fishers who had shot the seal mentioned its obvious sickness and apparent deafness, Another man, a trawler skipper from the east who had travelled there to buy a new boat, questioned him closely about the seal's symptoms, then told of similar incidents in his home waters. More fishermen joined the company and soon it became clear that sickness among seals was widespread. As the two drove back through the countryside to the ferry pier they talked some more of the disease and its implications. They were concerned, worried even, for they knew that in the sea what affected one Kind might soon spread to others, and their way of life, their livelihoods, might be at risk. They reached home and unloaded and cleaned their empty boxes, then went to the beach to see if the beast they had shot was washed up there, but found only the other animal which was without the mark of their bullet. Their minds on this new disease, they returned home for spades and buried the seal as deep as they could dig below the shingle.

Rondo had looked long and hard at the dead beast, for she knew the stench in her nose but could not place it. No healing kelp could have cured this animal, for the rot had not been in a flesh wound but deep inside the seal, a tiny organism which had so multiplied, become so pervasive of every organ and so powerful that the creature it inhabited was defenceless against its remorseless progress.

The organism was carried among the seals not so much by contact with each other but by tides and currents. The ocean has no boundaries, so all were threatened, and close to that threat, now, was Rondo One-Eye. She moved back from the dead beast, not frightened by it but suspicious. Taking to the water she looked back, almost as though expecting the seal to follow her. Daylight was breaking along the ridges and she swam out of the bay, setting her head purposefully towards a low point a few miles away at the western end of the island. By the time she had travelled a hundred seal's lengths, the dead animal was all but forgotten.

Rondo was hungry and dived deep to explore the bottom of Big Firth close to the small headland she had made for on

leaving the bay. Using her nose and whiskers she searched
gaps and crevices for signs of fish, and stalked the beds of
wrack and kelp hoping to frighten something from among
their fronds. But she found little; all seemed bare of food, so
she surfaced and made for a dark, weed-stained islet which
lay a short distance from the point.

She swam round, checking for other seals and looking for
the easiest place on which to haul out. Opposite, on the north
side of Big Firth was a high ridge, bright now, almost pink as
the low sun struck on wilting brown heather and was diffused.
The ridge was sharp, almost level until it ran down to its
seaward edge where black, jagged cliffs held back the ocean.
From there, in a wide arc from just west of north to south-
west, the horizon was unmarked by land, and for more than
one hundred degrees of the compass there was only open sea.
The seal hauled high on the rock to a place from which she
had the best, seaward view. The day was turning brighter and
she knew she would find little moving under the waves in
shallow water with such glare from the sun. Better to rest and
wait before exploring and looking for a safer, less exposed
resting rock before darkness fell, for then, as the sun sank and
the sky became tinged with red, fish would begin to move.

The energy Rondo needed to stay alive could be found
only through food. True, the thick layer of blubber she had
built up while taking Rainha's milk would, if necessary,
sustain her, but in the long term she must learn the skills
which enabled her to feed regularly and keep growing. Every
gram of energy she used in hunting had not only to be
replaced in full, but, as with the Kind of every bird and
beast, must be backed up by an additional amount to act as
a reserve. Only in such a way would she survive her first
winter and continue towards maturity. The waters round the
Islands of Lorne, washed as they were by the North Atlantic
Drift, were rich in fish and other life, and after a few days
Rondo became familiar with the place and began to catch
food fairly easily. She fell into a loose routine, exploring new
places for a few hours every day, now more relaxed and confident that she could feed herself without too great an effort.
She put on weight. Untroubled now by having only one eye,

if anything she grew more alert, more aware of possible dangers than many of her Kind. She took few chances and trusted nothing she did not know. In the Way of The Ages, such lack of trust should stand her in good stead.

She knew nothing of disease. She knew of pain and the dread smell and hot touch of man, but the dead seal she had come so close to was, to her and any other of her Kind, quite simply, a dead seal. The manner of its death had no significance. Rondo had left and kept clear of the bay where she had seen the dead beast, not because of its memory but because she had found no food there and had been disturbed by a noise she was unable to explain. She had missed the herring shoals by a few days. Now they were gone until the following year and she knew by The Ages that her time was better spent among the rocks and skerries outside the bay, and that to find a resting rock close to those feeding grounds was a way of saving energy and guarding her reserves.

Each morning now she saw the two fishermen, for she used several resting places close to the granite skerry where she had hauled out first after leaving the bay, all of which gave her a wide, seaward view and were close to her favoured fishing grounds. The weather changed. Wind blew steadily from the north-west and snow dusted the long ridge across Big Firth as winter's grip hardened. The fishermen watched the mountaintops as the snowline dropped steadily lower and lower. The crabs they now fished for needed fresh bait, rather than the salted fish they used for prawn or lobster, so they still used their nets every three or four days, not for herring but for other Kinds which could be found where Rondo fished along the hard ground close to the shore. As the species of fish they now sought had changed, so, too, had their method of catching them, and the long drift nets with which they encircled herring shoals had been replaced by lengths of tangled nylon, called trammels, which lay weighted on the bottom to form a lethal barrier to anything which tried to pass. They needed few such lengths, for not only were the tangles of nylon filament strong and binding, but the whole net, because of the material from which it was made, was invisible to any creature.

One morning Rondo had made her way to a favourite place beneath a high, weathered cliff where the seabed was uneven and thickly strewn with weed. Though not the easiest place in which to hunt, the tide ran gently over most of it and the tall weed waved gently in the slight current, breaking a seal's outline. Her mind and good eye sharp and ready for the slightest swirl, Rondo arrived below the cliff and first, floated lazily, looking down to check for other seals or anything else which might affect the hunt. Seeing her way clear she dived, following the line of the cliff to the bottom where she hung motionless for a few moments at the edge of the weed before moving slowly towards her killing ground. A cormorant flashed past her, diving for small fishes, and Rondo lunged, twisting and baring her bright, white teeth, not wishing to attack and kill the bird, but warning it off so she could hunt in peace.

She moved almost imperceptibly, calm again as soon as the cormorant had fled. She drifted forward, corkscrewing slowly as was now her habit, and stopping occasionally, allowing her long whiskers to sense the movements of tide and weed. After a few minutes, without warning she turned sharply and drove hard into the weed a seal's length below. Leaving a bursting, muddy cloud, a large, dark fish streaked from the spot the seal had targeted and swam, weaving through the rocks and reefs towards the darker water under the cliff face. Rondo recovered quickly from the miss, and glancing round, saw the creature as it disappeared into the shadows. She gave chase, not at full speed but at a pace which would allow her to turn rapidly if she flushed her quarry. Along the sheer face, hugging the wall of rock closely, she searched with every sense and muscle tensed, ready for the final, killing drive. Again the fish flushed away, this time well ahead of the seal, panicking and swimming hard alongside the submerged edge of the cliff giving itself little room to jink and dodge as the seal gathered pace and grew closer.

The sheer line of rock changed direction sharply to the south, but the fish in its panic to escape failed to follow the bend and instead swam straight on, out into the open and well above the sea floor. Rondo had all the time she needed now, and was almost assured of her meal as she tailed the saithe, confusing it and waiting for its final, reckless turn or panic-stricken dash to the surface before she struck and filled her belly. Then, without warning the fish stopped suddenly, thrashing wildly as though it had been held somehow, and Rondo, not knowing why the saithe had halted, drove hard for the kill. Even as the pup's small, white teeth closed around the flesh that was to feed her, She felt the net close round her, already burning and tearing her skin.

* * *

After shooting their trammel net the two fishermen had left to haul crab pots which lay some distance away. The net they had left was marked at either end with a large, red buoy which could be seen in almost any weather from a good distance. They lifted the first string of pots, one hauling on the winch then emptying the catch into a box, the other rebaiting the empty creels and stacking them neatly, ready to be shot away again when all ten on the string had been hauled and re-baited. Each had to concentrate hard in order to keep time with the other. Half way through the line of creels the baiter looked up, checking their distance from the rocks. He shouted to his companion, pointing towards the cliff where their trammel net was shot. "Look", he yelled, "Look at the buoy."

They watched as the red ball first disappeared then rose again as though being towed by something. Again it went down, now almost under the waves and being dragged strongly across the wind. "Shoot away", called the man at the hauler, already pushing the gear lever forward and reaching for the throttle. The boat sped forward and the creels were thrown over one by one as their connecting rope snaked out over the gunwale. As the last pot hit the water and the long end of line and its marker buoy were thrown into the wake, the boat was turned, heading now for the trammel net at full power. They did not pause to discuss what might be in the net but knew instinctively that whatever was there must be quite close to the buoy which still raced about across the surface. The movement was slowing, and the men knew that what was caught was already weakening, and whether a shark, a seal or dolphin, may well be dead by the time they could lift it clear: and lift they must, for they might lose the net completely if it were left alone. They snatched the moving buoy with the boathook and hauled it aboard, slamming the rope over the winding drum of the hauler before it had a chance to be towed from them, and even now, feeling the sharp tugging on the rope that could only mean something strong and heavy was entangled and trying desperately to break free.

Beneath the boat, Rondo thrashed violently, her teeth still locked to the saithe by the power of the net wrapped around her nose and head. She was already cut and bleeding. The net burned worse than the beaks of a thousand Eye-Peckers. Her air was almost used and she was desperate to rise and breathe; but still she thrashed, still The Ages called to her to fight for her life. She felt herself being drawn upwards, and in dazed panic drove back towards the bottom, seeing and understanding nothing, hearing only the sound of water around her, the rushing of blood that coursed in her on a deadly tide of panic. Water was in her lungs. She could not see. She tried to force her flippers through the net, tried to drive again, choking now, twisting and still writhing but powerless to save herself from the burning nylon, dying as The Ages called on her, even yet, to continue fighting.

Her ears filled with noise. With her lungs bursting and her energy almost completely sapped she no longer knew where she was or which way she faced as the terrible, confused sounds in her head reached, ever louder, into every corner of her brain. And then, it was gone. The seal fell limp, the fight gone from her, The Ages defeated as she lapsed into unconsciousness. The fishers still hauled. The net was tight as it came up over the drum but they could not see what had been caught in it and one stood ready with the rifle for shark or seal. The thrashing stopped, and as the net began to lift more smoothly the two looked at one another knowingly as though to confirm the beast was dead. Soon, the shape of a young seal, wrapped in a nylon shroud, broke surface and was hauled over the gunwale by strong arms to drop onto the deck and land, lying on its back.

Water ran from Rondo's throat and month. She was cut deeply round her nose where the thin, nylon strands had been tightest, and her blood left small, red spots on the deck around her. She had been seconds from complete unconsciousness, and now, as air was drawn into her lungs and she tried automatically to open her mouth against the now loosened net and breathe properly, she retched, jerking violently on the bottom boards as she tried to expel the water.

The fishermen were shocked by the sight, more so perhaps than if the seal had been already dead. They could not shoot Rondo there in the boat, for the heavy bullet would pierce the hull and they would sink. She lay on her back, gasping for as much air as she could take, and now, one of the men made to roll her over to see if they would be able to do anything for her. As her face was turned and the jagged cross over her left eye came into view he froze. "Look at this", he said, "It's just like that seal in the story."

His companion moved forward to look at the seal, and on seeing Rondo's face drew his knife and began to cut away the stretched nylon strands. He began at her tail and worked upwards, leaving the torn face till last so the pup would not be able to bite him as he worked. When she was freed they pulled the net from her and quickly shot it out over the side in case she struggled and became entangled a second time.

Rondo was dizzy and remembered nothing of what had happened to her. Her head hurt and the vibrations of the boat's engine ran through her body, confusing her still more as she spluttered and gasped her way back to consciousness. Her first sense of reality was to smell the saithe which had fallen from the net as it was cut away and now lay close to her on the deck, its head almost severed from its body. One of the fishers leaned over to pick it up, but thought better as he saw the pup's glazed eye looking at his hand as if gauging its distance from her teeth. The other man took Rondo by the tail flippers and pulled her to the back of the boat before going forward again to join his companion. They didn't know what to do with the seal. They didn't want to shoot it, but neither did they wish to return it straight to the water until it had recovered. They thought, too, that the pup might possibly be ill like the one they had shot a few days before, so were cautious of handling it.

Keeping their distance they peered curiously at their one-eyed captive. They knew all too well the ailments of sheep and cattle and the symptoms those beasts could show for any disease. They looked for anything in the seal pup apart from the injuries caused by the net and its healed eye wound that might point to what was wrong with it, but it looked healthy otherwise, and after some talk of what they should do they decided to return to their bay and carry the seal above the tideline where it might recover. As they made their way homeward they recalled the tale of The Silver Thread and its one-eyed seal. But this was no ghost they carried with them in the boat, it was a real, live beast and it began to worry them that their trammel net could so easily catch and injure creatures like seals and dolphins which caused them so much trouble and regret. They covered her head and body with an old oilskin, hoping in that way to keep her calm and not distress her too much.

Although her heart still raced with fright young Rondo lay still. She could hear the mens' voices above the engine noise but all she could do was try to catch her breath and gain some strength as the ordeal continued. She longed for the cooling waters of Big Firth, longed to feel them on the cuts around her muzzle and on her body, and though she could not see the water she could sense it, smell it above the smell of diesel, and hear it running along the hull of the boat as they sped back to the bay. She struggled as she was loaded into the dinghy and rowed ashore, but at least the throbbing of the engine had ceased, and she relaxed more as all she could now hear was the gentle creaking of the oars.

The skiff was pulled up above the high water mark and only then was Rondo lifted out and placed on the shingle. They lifted her again, still blinded by the oilskin coat and not knowing what was going to happen. Only as they placed her gently on a large slab of rock and pulled the covering away

did she see where she was. The men left immediately, not wishing to upset the beast further, and in any case, not keen to feel her teeth around their fingers. She lay still, unsure about her freedom and not knowing quite what to do. She was still dazed, but all the water was out of her lungs and her breath was restored, allowing her to think more clearly. The water beckoned. Slowly she began to move, and little by little, made her way down to the sea. She felt tired, no longer dizzy, but weary, as though the last two hours had aged her, and as she flopped gratefully into the shallow bay and swam slowly towards its entrance, all she wanted was a quiet spot and a long rest.

*   *   *

A few hours later Rondo had hauled above the tide on her favourite resting rock. Another seal was there, an old cow, much scarred by a long life, who eyed the still bleeding pup suspiciously. Rondo ignored the older beast. She was far enough away from her to avoid the pushing and flipper beating which sometimes happened when the aged met the very young, and was too tired anyway to do anything more than doze off. Luckily, the cuts she had suffered were not severe. They were painful, but the net had sliced cleanly into the flesh and had not sawed so much that the wounds had bitten too deep to heal quickly. In a day or two they would begin to close, and in a few weeks time she would have little to show for the experience but one or two slim scars. All depended now on whether she was still able to hunt and keep her belly filled.

She had burned up a lot of energy in her attempts to escape; far more than had been provided by the food she had taken over the past week, and she would have to eat soon. She dozed, keeping an eye on the sea around her, even more wary now after her latest battle. In an hour she woke, hungry and eager to hunt. Her attention was caught by the old cow at the far end of the rock. Something was not as it should be. The beast was retching quietly and struggled to draw breath. Her head lolled, moving slowly up and down as though controlled by a string, and her rear flippers lay flat to the rock, lifeless and spread out. Rondo did her best to ignore the stricken cow, but the noise of her breathing grew stronger and only when the beast retched did she appear to have any strength, arching her back with the effort then falling back on to the rock, her head flat to the stone. The pup could smell the old beast's breath. Rondo raised her head sharply as the stink came to her again: it was the stink of living death.

She launched quickly and swam into Big Firth. Clouds had begun to gather and all creatures knew of an approaching storm. Rondo knew she must eat then find a sheltered lair before the wind came, for it could be days before the gale blew itself out. She looked around at the islands which at first had seemed so welcoming, so complete in all she needed. For a moment she imagined that she scented again the death stink of the old cow and of the dead beast she had seen in the bay a few days before. She turned and looked north-east, and with a Message of The Ages rising in her mind, moved steadily towards The Narrows and her birthplace in Loch Shiel.

Chapter 11

Almost as soon as she had begun to make for The Narrows, Rondo's mind had become detached from the events of the last few days, and in the Way of The Ages she now concentrated only on the task in hand. She would hunt at Sallachan then take the flood tide through The Narrows before the gale struck. As she reached the flats she dived to the bottom, searching the mud with her nose and disturbing numerous small fish. She ate everything, no matter how small, and so single minded was she that within an hour her belly was as full as it could ever be. Without hesitating she made on towards her goal. The gale rose behind her in the west and the swell began to lift, long and oily but without the high crests the coming wind would build on them so quickly. From time to time the pup stopped to look back. She knew by The Ages that the storm would break on the coast as the flood tide turned and began to flow back towards the ocean. She sensed the changes in strength and direction and hurried on, knowing she had less than an hour to pass The Narrows and find a safe place to haul.

Currents boiled and swirled, pulling the one-eyed pup in all directions until she found the narrow strip of water which took the flood into Loch Shiel and she was carried through. The day blackened and the sea grew angry as the tide turned and began to ebb, but the pup was inside the loch, safe, provided she could find a place to haul clear of the fury closing in behind her. Black Rocks were barely visible. They were not the best place but she made for them, the only shelter she would find short of Birthing Rock or Bay of Otters, both a long way to travel with a gale building.

She chose a small skerry at the eastern edge of the Black Rocks group, one which afforded no real protection from the wind, but where the sea's power would be broken by the other rocks to windward. To the north-east, Dun Mountain was wreathed in cloud, already sweeping, rain-filled, along the line of the loch as the wind funnelled and grew in strength between the hills. Talon and Chryso were already settled on leeward ledges, out of the gale and watching as the streams below them grew and Dun Mountain corrie became filled with the sounds of wind and swiftly flowing water. The seal was tired. Her belly had been well filled but her time fighting the net and the long swim to Loch Shiel had depleted her reserves. What she needed more than anything was rest, more food and above all, peace. There was, too, something else which might affect her now, for over the past week she had been in close contact with two other seals, first, the one in the bay and then the old cow on the skerry. Both were now dead.

She hauled out as darkness enclosed the loch and the wind still rose. She moved at midnight to a larger islet, for the wind had turned to come from the north-west and was bitterly cold. She found an overhang and lay beneath it, warmer and safer there, knowing that a cold wind would steal her energy as effectively as any chase or entanglement with nets. As the fish she had taken at Sallachan worked in her she remained warm and deep asleep, recovering already.

In a single movement the pup twisted, lifting her head to look directly above. It was not the main clamour which had roused her but a single cry which rung out above all the others; a cry which raised such terror and anger in Rondo that even as she had begun to move she was already snarling, her teeth bared as the death call of the Eye-pecker echoed through the wind.

Day had broken and the sky appeared empty. The low ledge above her and the stunted pines behind blocked her view to the west, so she slid from her ledge and swam to the south side of the skerry to see where the noise had come from. The wind had dropped and the rain came now only in short pulses. Between the showers a seal's view from the top of a small wave was a clear one hundred lengths in each direction, and by the long, black reef from which the islands took their name, Rondo saw a great flock of Eye-Peckers wheeling above the loch, death in their raucous voices.

Rondo made towards them warily, curious as to why the birds were so excited. She could see nothing on the rock yet, so moved closer. She dived, surfacing again ten seal's lengths from the reef and ready to dive again if danger threatened. Beneath the gulls and grey crows was a seal; a bull of Rondo's Kind, old and heavy, wallowing as though helpless in the shallows. Above him, were at least two dozen Eye-Peckers.

The pup eyed the older animal, keeping her distance and wondering why the Eye-Peckers should pay such a large beast so much attention. He was only a seal's length from the reef, and as Rondo grew closer he made as if to haul out, then seemed to change his mind at the last minute and sank back into the loch. The birds were all around him, swirling in the breeze, cawing and screaming. Again he went to haul, but as he lifted himself onto the rock with his front limbs his head dropped flat onto the rock and he slid heavily backwards.

Only a few weeks before the bull had been content enough. He was not a native of Loch Shiel but had mated here in some summers. He was a roamer, leaving wherever he found himself in early spring and travelling, sometimes for great distances, around the western coastline. He had seen many places and, in the Way of The Ages, was skilled in hunting having learned much in his wanderings.

Although by choice a solitary animal, occasionally, the bull would haul out with other seals, passing greetings in the tongue of his Kind, telling that he meant no harm and would soon be gone. That summer, before mating time he had returned to Loch Shiel, but soon afterwards had moved out through The Narrows and headed south beyond the waters of Big Firth to where the coast became flat and low lying, and towns and cities pour filth into the sea.

He had halted by a long headland he knew as a gathering place of many Leapers and Tail Shakers, all newly run from

Greenland's sea. The headland was their lighthouse. It marked a place for them to wait, gathering with their kin before turning to make towards their birth streams. Seals came there from far places, joining those which lived on the beaches and small skerries of the headland in the rich, passing harvest. In the way of The Ages this yearly bounty was also a time for the mixing of blood, and many of the seals that travelled there, particularly younger beasts, remained to mate before returning to their home waters. But if life could come from such meetings and the Kind of any creature be strengthened by new blood, so, too, could death and weakness spread. At the great harvest of the headland, and a thousand like it in every sea where seals are gathered, danger, unseen and unrecognised, travelled with them.

The bull had mated then left to follow the Leapers back to Loch Shiel. Now, his every move was torture to him. First his throat had swollen so he had been unable to eat without choking. After a few days, every stroke he swam and every breath he drew racked him with pain. His joints became stiff and his eye sockets and nostrils swelled and were filled with stinking fluid. He could no longer hunt and hunger grew in him then stopped as his thick blubber converted to energy and was used to keep him alive. The disease raged in him and his mind became numb until the only thing he knew in those last hours, those final minutes, was to fight.

As Rondo swam across the loch the bull tried once more to gain the reef. He looked round and saw through blurred eyes the twin spires of Dun Mountain and the steep fall of ground into the bays and deeps of Loch Shiel. The cry of the Eye-Peckers was still above him, and this time, even as he touched the reef and began to haul, the birds stooped, tumbling through the wind to mob the stricken beast. Their cries were all he could hear now. He could no longer see. He needed rest but refused to give in to the longest rest of all for the Voice of The Ages was with him, and he turned to face the Eye-Peckers, his last breath expelled in anger in a long, defiant bark. Then, rolling, lunging at the birds, he sank into Loch Shiel, down into the seaward current to lie forever among the bones of his ancestors.

Chapter 12

Somehow, Rondo knew that the bull had died. Her mind had begun to connect the events of the last week, though she did not think in the way men think, nor reason in their way; but still, she was aware that all was not well with her Kind. She wanted none of it, and just as she had left Big Firth after the others had died, now she knew that she had to get as far from Black Rocks as she could. Under the shadow of Dun Mountain she dived, sinking slowly until the surface light was lost completely and her eye focussed in a different way, gathering every glimmer through the thousand tiny mirrors that were in its living globe. This was not a world of colour to the seal, but one of movement and contrast where every swirl and change of line or form had meaning. She hunted slowly, not hungry but knowing her reserves had been depleted and she must replace what had been lost. Her search was painstaking and systematic, and every crevice, every bed of weed was explored thoroughly. Following the line of the shore she nosed and probed with her whiskers until each hiding place was searched, surfacing every five minutes or so, not needing breath after such a short time but watching, mindful of the ways of seabirds which could alert her to shoals of fish.

The sky was clear of any bird, and by now even the Eye-Peckers that had mobbed the old bull had moved away. Rondo dived again, following the line of the shore and searching in the same, unhurried way. She came to the wide bay where Rainha had taught her to dig out prawns, and settled at the side of a large rock, close to the edge of the muddy strip where she knew that the pink creatures had their burrows. The rock was uneven, breaking her outline and the water was deep so no light filtered from above. Her eye focussed rapidly on the muddy floor of the loch, her head, as always, was held slightly to the left.

She hung motionless but for the slightest movement as each limb was used to hold her in position. A few large prawns were feeding about five seal's lengths from her and she knew she might have to dig them out since the ground between her and their burrows was open and the prawns were lightning fast when escaping. She waited, ranging the prawns, knowing she would have to move quickly if she was to take one before they had all shot deep into their holes. She tensed, ready to spring, but then, just as she was about to drive her attention was taken by a faint, disappearing glimmer not far to her right. She held back, swivelling and fixing her eye on the point where she had seen the movement. There was nothing there: even though the ground was open and bare of weeds or rocks she could see nothing. Something odd had happened, something she didn't fully understand but which The Ages told her to investigate.

She didn't move from the shelter of the rock but stared hard at the place. A small fish approached the spot, swimming slowly towards what looked like a small, fleshy morsel, hanging in the water just above the bottom. It was a good meal for a small fish, and it continued to approach, intent on taking what was offered. But as it drew within striking distance, within a split second the fish was gone, and only then did Rondo see the grotesque, wide mouth and rows of white, needle sharp teeth as the angler fish gulped a second time then sank back into its depression in the mud. As soon as it was hidden again, camouflaged by the muddy colour of its wide, almost flat back, the fatal bait was dangled once again from the thin, transparent spine which pointed outwards like a fishing rod from the top of its head.

Fascinated, the pup watched as two more fish were caught and devoured in the same way. She could not see the angler fish's body, but the mouth was as wide as the length of one of Rondo's front flippers, a needle-filled cavern of death for any fish that came within its range, and which made the pup think hard about the risk involved in catching it. Slowly, she moved forward, carefully staying directly between the rock and the angler fish's line of sight so she would remain in cover. As she moved ahead the monster took another fish, and yet again she saw the gaping mouth and backward slanting teeth.

She moved back a little, fanning her front limbs to bring her further into the shelter of the big stone. Once there she turned very slowly, with no sudden moves that might create even the slightest swirl of mud, then drew behind the stone and drifted along the bottom a short distance before rising to the surface to draw breath. Without looking round she sank again to the bottom, this time making sure she landed where she knew she was well behind the angler but not too far to find it easily. Once she saw the creature she gauged its distance, and hung, two seal's lengths above the bottom. By now, despite the pup's stealth the angler fish had sensed danger and had folded its fishing rod down along the line of its back and snugged into its depression so it was all but invisible. But Rondo's eye was already fixed on the spot and she nosed forward, now closer and more able to judge the true size of the fish. She saw that it was almost triangular in shape, the great wide mouth enabling it to grab food over a wide arc without having to move more than a few lengths from its hideout. Behind the huge, ugly head the body tapered to a thin, narrow tail, almost finless, for since most of its time was spent in the mud of the seabed, its Kind had little need of streamlined bodies or of powerful, driving tails.

To Rondo the creature was a mystery, and as close as she now was to it, so well camouflaged was the fish that she had to concentrate hard to keep her eye on where it lay. Unsure, she moved closer until only a seal's length behind it and a little above, not knowing how to tackle the brute, whether to drive hard or to sneak up and make a quick grab, hoping to avoid the teeth. The Ages spoke of caution, but she knew she would have to move soon or risk losing her meal. She lifted a little, giving herself room, then, twisting slightly so she would come at the fish from the side, she drove down.

She caught the angler squarely across the back then rolled

and shook it hard. The pressure of the huge head being jerked from side to side severed its spine, and by the time Rondo had the fish on the surface it was no longer even flapping. She leaned back in the water to strip flesh from the angler's back, holding it with her front flippers and no longer worried by its twin rows of sharp teeth. She left little of her catch for the gulls which had gathered above her, but even as she dropped the skeletal remains and swam away, the birds dived, screaming, racing to be first to catch the carcase before it sank to the mud for crabs and starfish to finish it off.

Within half an hour Rondo was hauled out, cleaning herself with her front claws to remove every trace of flesh from her whiskers and face. A new lesson had been learned, one of great benefit to a seal for most angler fish were large and fleshy. A few hours later she was back, close to where she had caught the first fish, looking for another, and by nightfall her belly was full. She had caught two more, one so much larger than the first that much of it had been left for the creatures of the loch bottom. She lay again on South Shore in the lee of Deer Grass Point, sheltered from a breeze which had veered east and carried the cold scents of winter.

In the earliest hours of the next morning she was wakened by coughing and the laboured sounds of heavy breath. Focussing quickly, she looked across the beach and saw another seal hauling out slowly and with obvious difficulty. She murmured a low greeting to warn the beast of her presence and tried to settle again, but the other seal continued coughing and the pup became more and more distracted. The beast had stopped only halfway up the shingle, still within the tide's reach and not even having bothered to turn and face towards the loch. The coughing stopped and the beast lay flat, its head and neck stretched out on the small stones and its limbs lifeless, seemingly without the strength to haul further.

Rondo dozed, but was disturbed often by the other seal further along the beach. Before dawn the wind dropped, but as first light crossed the slopes it rose again, now from the north-west in cool and gentle gusts and carrying a stench that brought Rondo to full wakefulness, for in her nostrils, once again, there was the stink of death. This time she did not wait, but turned and threw herself headlong down the shallow slope and into the sea. Without looking back she dived and swam towards the deeps. The stench was still in her nose and only when she was almost half way across Loch Shiel did she surface and turn back nervously to face the shore. She was frightened. All the events of the past days since she had seen the first, dead beast had come together, building her comprehension and bringing a growing awareness that all was not as it should be; that once again her life, somehow, was under threat. Winter was almost upon the Northlands. It was not the best time for such distraction, nor was it the time of year for any beast to become sick.

Chapter 13

For a few days she hunted in the loch, shunning the company of others and still nervous that the death stench would come to her again. Each day grew shorter as the sun continued its decline, and every evening now, red deer were to be found among the shelter of the lochside trees as they escaped the chill winds. Birch and oak and ash grew bare, and their leaves fell to rot and enrich the ground. Rondo watched the changing colours of Dun Mountain and saw long, craggy shadows creep across the highest slopes as each day's end approached and clouds were set afire by a hardening, unwarming sun.

The pup was unsure of herself, for the events of the past few weeks had made it seem as though all her Kind were stricken in some way, unsafe; each one, in ways she could not reason with, a danger to her. Instinctively she knew this was her home, that she should be comfortable here, inside The Narrows where there were familiar sights and places; places where she should be able to haul and rest in safety and which were, or should have been in normal times, hers by right of The Ages to use unhindered. But it seemed now that each waking hour had to be spent avoiding those places she had learned of at her mother's side, for each now appeared to carry all the signs of death.

Disconsolately, Rondo moved gradually eastwards towards Bay of Shelters, troubled and fearing contact with other seals. But even as she travelled she felt her heart and breath quicken slightly. A strange dryness had come to her throat. She weaved a little as she swam, finding it hard to concentrate on the direction she had to follow. She passed

Sword Island and was tired, her throat now sore. By the time she hauled on Resting Rock she was dizzy, desperate for sleep.

★   ★   ★

Two hundred seal's lengths across Bay of Shelters from the pup, another seal lay hauled onto the rough beach. The beast was barely breathing. The pain was past. The coughing and gasping for breath through pain-racked lungs was over. The dizziness, too, was gone, and all the days and nights of hunger, of being unable to hunt through lack of strength, all these things were but a memory, and as the seal lay on those sharp, black stones she felt no discomfort, for her world had become a dull haze. Her memory was blurred but in her mind's eye she saw now others of her Kind around her. She heard them call as beasts had called throughout The Ages since the days of The Seal Fathers and she fought, fought for consciousness so she might greet them again in the tongue of their Kind.

The beast hauled round to face Loch Shiel and The Island of Swords where most of the best days and hours of her life had been spent. In a final, brave effort to conquer death she tried to make towards the sea, forcing air into swollen, fluid filled lungs to give herself a few seconds of strength and allow her to raise her head, as though listening for The Ages to speak and send her their last, inevitable Message.

After moving only half a seal's length, the stricken beast slumped, unable to continue further. For a few moments her vision cleared a little. Above Dun Mountain the sky was red; bright red, as red as blood and redder now; and the ridges of Talon's crag were black, so much blacker and more distinct than she had ever seen them. But how the day faded so quickly: how soon the light had died and night had come. With early darkness in her failing eyes the seal lowered her head to the stones. Her breath was no more than a whisper. She could no longer see but she rebelled. And with her last breath, still, she rebelled, her head lifted in one final gasp, calling; calling for the light to return, calling to all the

Lessons and Messages of The Ages and to The Seal Fathers. Rainha, mother cow of Rondo One-Eye, was dead.

Chapter 14

On Resting Rock, across Bay of Shelters from where her mother's body lay, Rondo woke to the screech of Strix. Low, freezing mist hung like a shroud above the loch and the night air was still and heavy with moisture. The young seal shivered. She breathed heavily into lungs which now felt as though they were filled with fire. Her nose and good eye were becoming useless, so full were they of the plague's poisons. Each time she moved, trying to find comfort or relief, she gasped in agonizing pain. A war raged in her: the sickness drove her ever more deeply into shock and with the cold, drew heavily on her last reserves of heat and energy. Hunger, too, gnawed her spirit; pain and cold and hunger; each her enemy; now joined as one with the sickness that was in her, more deadly than a thousand Eye-Peckers or the strongest of all storms.

But, suddenly, The Ages spoke: Rondo raised herself and turned towards the sea, ignoring pain. She launched down the slope of Resting Rock, and as the sea began to cradle her felt the pain ease. It was warmer in the water – much warmer than in the freezing air above – and for the first time in many days she was able to swim slowly along the north side of Sword Island. She spied below the surface as she made her way so that her eye keened a little, tuning mind and muscle as far as the disease allowed. She dived steeply to the kelpen reef with the Messages of The Ages in her every movement, for to live, Rondo One-Eye must eat within the next few hours.

★   ★   ★

By the shores of Loch Shiel and in the wider world far from the Northlands, word had been abroad for many months of the plague which decimated Rondo's Kind. The disease, similar to the distemper found in dogs, was at its worst in the shallow waters of the eastern sea, where, for centuries the hand of man had cast the filth of his Kind. And in that sea, where the Kind of Rondo and Rainha had lived in peace before men stood straight, seals died in their thousands, swept by the plague like blossom before a spring gale.

Predictably, men denied that the problem had been caused by them. It had been a natural thing, something which just, – happens. The voices of those who disagreed were soon drowned by a flood of information from governments and corporations which, they said, proved there could be no link between "Seal plague" as the disease was becoming known, and the continuing pollution of the seas and oceans of the world. More importantly perhaps, it was stated that there was no risk to man of infection by contact with a sick seal. The fuss died away when this was known, and the fate of the seals was left in the hands of small groups of dedicated people who did what they could for any stricken beasts that could be rescued.

At the edge of the Village, between Owl Oaks and Boat Bay stood a small, white-painted house where lived a deerstalker and his wife. The bloodlines of both their families were written large on the history of Loch Shielside, and since the days of Harvester, through war and peace, through famine and during times of plenty, not they nor any of their forefathers had seen anything like the plague which afflicted the seals of this clean, western shore.

The stalker lived in nature. He was part of it, replacing wolf and bear and tiger, all long since exterminated by the hand of man. Such beasts as these had been the predators of deer, thinning herds according to the Laws of The Ages; taking the weak, infirm and injured or those less careful than they should have been. Without these predators the great herds could only increase, grazing until famine was across the land and they died in their thousands in hard winters. After the last of the wolves had been killed, men hunted deer with dogs, driving them into blind gorges, over cliffs or onto rough shores where they might kill them with spears or arrows, and for centuries deer were harvested in this way, more brutal than the natural chase of a pack of wolves whose purpose was to single out the weakest. At last the bullet came, and for once the ingenuity of man seemed to have triumphed over his brutality, for the heavy ball was swift and strong, killing a beast before it had even heard the weapon being fired. When the stalker of Loch Shielside went about his duties on the hill, he knew all these things.

It had been his wife who had found Rainha's body on the shore, coming across the dead seal lying on the strand in Bay of Shelters as she took her evening walk with their dogs. In the dusk she had looked over the bay to Resting Rock, and seeing a pup lying there had hoped it was not the one-eyed beast she had watched over the past months and grown fond of, for if the seal she had just found had, as she thought, died of plague, then the pup, too, might be infected.

Her husband, no stranger to sickness in bird and beast, was at first sceptical about whether the seal had died of plague. Over the years he had come to consider such things carefully and his faith in nature's power to recover from disasters had been vindicated season upon season. Often, there would be little outward sign of sickness or disease in living things, and whether it was grouse or mountain hare which died in great numbers, they had always recovered; normality, nature, had always reigned again after a few summers.

More recently, though, things had seemed to change. There was little he could point to on the land, but Leaper and Tail Shaker were becoming less and less numerous and no longer crammed the holding pools of Rough River after the autumn spates. The seasons, too, were changing. Over forty years ago when the stalker had begun work, assisting his father on the hill, snow would begin to fall on the tops in October, and would remain there, deepening to the height of a man in the most shaded corries until the snowmelt of March and April. Winter frosts had, in the past, been long and brittle, hardening the ground for weeks on end and holding the snow until, in the lengthening spring days, it ran

clean as purging meltwater. Now, it seemed as if there was
no real winter any more, and even in January or February
when the highest tops should be white with snow, it was not
unusual to see them black and bare. In a few years time the
stalker would retire. He had begun to want that time, that
day, for he was puzzled and concerned by all the changes he
saw. In his heart he felt that he had seen the last of the
natural world as nature had meant it be, and in the long term
he saw little hope for the dear land where his family had lived
and toiled happily for so many centuries.

He had walked the shore to where Rainha lay and looked
carefully at the carcase. Seal plague had been in the news for
months but he had believed, – he had hoped, that it would
never come to this clean, lovely place. What had killed this
animal, he wondered. The seal lay at his feet, her eyes and
nostrils caked with foul mucus and her neck grotesquely
swollen. His wife had mentioned the undersized, one-eyed
pup, but his torch beam scarcely reached to Resting Rock
from where he stood. He could not be certain, but deep in
his heart he knew intuitively that plague had killed the cow,
and if the one-eyed pup had been near the dead beast there
was a better than fair chance that soon, it too, would die. He
knew his wife would want him to search by boat in the
morning for any sign of her favourite. He gave a last sad
glance at the dead cow, and as he walked homewards
resolved to take a rifle with him the following day, for if the
pup or any other seal he came across appeared sick, it would
be kinder to give the beast a quick, painless end than to leave
it to suffer such a miserable death.

By the time he returned home his wife had already been in
touch with the vet who had arranged for Rainha's body to be
removed and examined. If other seals were found which
might be caught, they could, the vet said, be taken south to
a sanctuary where they would be treated and might, if strong
enough, recover.

★   ★   ★

Rondo had felt the heavy coat being thrown across her

back but had not found strength enough to snap or even growl at the human she knew was there but could not see. She felt herself being lifted and then placed gently on the bottom-boards of the boat. Water ran along the outside of the hull close to her ear and then, after the keel had hissed on to the shingle beach below the stalker's house, once again she felt herself being lifted and carried by her captor. She tried to struggle but was powerless, all her energy spent, and by the time she had been placed on the stone floor of the outhouse, she had all but lost consciousness.

The stalker had found her draped over the top of Whale Rock. When he had come to within a boat length of the pup and realised she was alive but stricken, he had raised his rifle, aimed at her head and pushed the safety catch off with his thumb, the first finger of his right hand ready to squeeze the trigger. He should have fired, killing the seal instantly with a shot to her head. But he had not done that. Something had held him, had said, no, and the safety catch was pulled back and the rifle replaced on the seat.

That evening, the woman who had come to collect Rainha's carcase was taken to the outhouse to examine the pup. She had only glanced at Rondo. It's seal plague. I'm certain of it!" she said. "She's very bad, I'm afraid. I don't think she'll survive the journey."

Chapter 15

Rondo looked up from the pool at the sea of human faces that all but encircled her. So many, all watching her every move as she swam first this way, then the other, along the twenty or so seal's lengths of space which was all she had to move around in. She no longer feared them as she had in the beginning, and now even the noise didn't frighten her too much, although when arms were waved or pointed suddenly towards her, The Ages still warned of weapons and she would dive suddenly, only to find her escape stopped short by the shallow, rectangular confines of her pool.

Of what lay beyond those narrow margins she could see nothing, and her only association with anything that had been part of her existence before were the sounds and scents of the sea that carried in on the wind. But though she knew the sea was close she could taste nothing of its riches in her clean, chemically treated cell: nor could she know its boundless freedom, hers by right, gifted to all her Kind by The Ages. Food was brought to her four times daily, and at two of those times, a few hours before and after the sun was at full height, there were usually many more faces than at other times of day. Rondo now recognised the three people who, at various times, carried the pails of fish to her, and had quickly grown able to anticipate their arrival, for the routine had been much the same at the place where she had been before being brought here. But in that other place, instead of only human faces she had known also the company of many other seals, and in that had found some comfort; some security and less confusion.

Rondo had been snatched from death, then very slowly had been nursed back to health only to be trapped again, prevented from returning to the wild by those same creatures who had brought about her recovery. The care and kindness of those such as the stalker's wife of Loch Shielside was now replaced by greed and avarice; for in this beast, in this undersized, one-eyed seal, somebody had seen financial opportunity.

The pup remembered nothing of the long journey from Loch Shielside, for she had lain unconscious in the rear of the station wagon as the hills of the Northlands slipped by, unnoticed as they disappeared into the far distance and the land around became flat and featureless. Her awakening was not to come for days, for she hung on the edge of death until the kindness and patience of the woman who ran the sanctuary to which she had been brought, prevailed, and slowly the seal began to gather strength. The woman and her helpers had marvelled at the way the one-eyed pup had fought the plague. When other seals less badly afflicted succumbed and slipped from life, Rondo had held on, almost as though in limbo, breathing so lightly that at times the woman had to check carefully to make sure the seal was still alive. It was not the first time she had fought for her life; and those other trials must have helped as the Lessons of The Ages carried her, day by day, until at last the Plague's poisons tired of the fight and backed away.

Slowly, she awakened. She was too weak to know or care about where she might be, too uncomprehending to object in physical ways by snarling or baring her teeth when the woman or her assistants came near. Her first inklings of reality came as she was fed and began to taste the fish mulch which spilled from the funnel by which it entered her gullet. As she became more conscious and found some energy, – enough at least to spit at her captors, it became dangerous to feed Rondo in this way, and the woman quickly realised that the pup's alarm must have been caused by some well remembered, unpleasant experience involving humans. She wondered how the pup had been so badly injured and when visitors came to the sanctuary, pointed to the ragged scars as an example of how strong some animals must be that they could survive injuries which would kill most men.

The mulch was replaced by small pieces of fish and then by whole mackerel or herring, a rich, restorative diet to build up her reserves of fat and energy. Rondo became progressively more interested in her surroundings as her strength increased. She grew familiar with the woman and her helpers who struggled hard to feed the large number of seals which had become their responsibility. Through this familiarity she became more tractable, and, rather dangerously, began in a small but still suspicious way to associate the human form with food. Although the woman tried to make sure that she and her helpers never became too fond of their charges, they spoke gently to the seals to calm them as they went about their chores, and some animals began to trust them, perhaps too well for their own future well-being, for few men act under such kindly motives as those who laboured so hard on behalf of the plagued seals.

For a long time the sanctuary had been a haven to lost, abandoned or ill-used birds and beasts of all Kinds. Many seal pups, found on beaches or among rocks by holiday makers who assumed they were lost or had been abandoned by their mothers, arrived at the sanctuary, perhaps after having spent some hours or even days in someone's bath. Many were lost causes, victims of shock brought on by their removal from familiar surroundings and lack of milk, and soon died. Over the years the woman who struggled to run the sanctuary had come to handle many such seals, gaining something of a reputation for being able to effect a cure where others might fail. When seal plague struck in the eastern sea her knowledge, experience and skills were put to good use, and within a short time over a hundred seals of all ages and degrees of sickness were under her care. All had to be fed, all medicated, accommodated and kept clean. The sanctuary became a victim of the woman's patience and dedication, for from its beginning it had been funded solely through the generosity of concerned individuals who heard of its fine work and felt strongly that the place should continue. But it was expensive, and now, with so many seals to look after it had become a hard, slogging battle against the rising cost of time, food and medication.

For Rondo and the other seals the sanctuary became their home. It was almost as if they could sense that, in the way they were treated there, there was nothing of which they need be afraid, nothing that any Message of The Ages could warn of or caution against. They were fed regularly, had the company of other seals and, when sufficiently recovered to be put out in the open, had a large if somewhat crowded pool in which to play and wallow. They knew nothing of the problems which pervaded the working life of the place in which they found themselves, where now, every moment of the day was filled as much by worry as by what had always been the woman's driving motivation, the joy of playing a part in the recovery, or at least comfort of, something which otherwise would have no hope. From governments and giant corporations whose wastes and filth had contributed so much to foul the oceans, the sanctuary received little more than token offerings, and though individuals continued to be generous of time, money and equipment, the enormous costs became a burden which was borne with increasing difficulty.

It had always been intended that every seal should be returned to the ocean when recovered. It soon became a necessity, for as a seal approached full health under the care and dedication which was its good fortune to enjoy, its appetite grew apace, and the supply of prime, fresh fish required to maintain its rate of progress became almost impossible to sustain. Things became so bad, the sanctuary's bankers so difficult, there was a real danger the place would have to close. Help was needed. The press launched an appeal which held off the bank, but the long term problem of keeping so many seals persisted and the woman would not compromise by reducing rations or taking any other measure which might affect their recovery. But, luckily, word had got around, and soon a number of other establishments which could offer food but, sometimes, not the skills and high levels of care required by newly plagued animals, offered to take seals which were in the final stages of recovery and almost ready for release.

Rondo had not been one of the first to go, though many others still remained after her departure. Despite being smaller than her peers it was felt that she was somehow harder and more capable, more mature than others of her age, and would benefit much less from being kept any longer than from an early release. Two men came who had, it seemed, the ideal place, a small, marine centre only a stone's throw from the sea on the southern coast of the country. There, they said, the one-eyed seal would be well looked after. The place had a good supply of fresh fish, a pool fed by the sea; everything, in fact, which would bring the pup quickly to a point where she could be taken to the Northlands by car and released, fit and healthy, back into her home waters. The woman was delighted. With all the long hours of work involved in keeping the sanctuary running smoothly she never thought to check on anyone who offered help, and in any case, generally took people at face value. The two men who offered Rondo a home and then release appeared genuine and had done nothing to cause the woman any doubt they would do anything other than what they said.

In such a way had Rondo become a prisoner again, for the one-eyed pup was a natural, a real crowd puller. Marketed, advertised; the owners quickly realised that Rondo One-Eye could make them rich. They came in droves to marvel at the one-eyed seal. They were told through a loudspeaker of how she held her head slightly to one side and how the wound had probably been caused by a bullet. The woman at the sanctuary came to hear how her former charge was being used, but at first thought little of it; after all, it had been only a week or two since the beast had left her. But weeks turned into months and there was still no sign that Rondo was about to be released. There were no other exhibits at the centre besides Rondo except a souvenir shop where pink, fluffy seals could be bought for several times their worth. Rondo was the star, the main and only attraction which, each evening at counting up time, put smiles across the faces of the two men who now "owned" her.

★   ★   ★

She was a prisoner and perhaps she sensed that. All she was required to do was to swim up and down, rolling, turning, lying on her back, then, when she heard the clanging of the fish bucket, surge forward to catch the mackerel which would be thrown to her as the gaping mouths of the paying masses made strange, unnatural noises. When she had eaten she would swim again as the crowd dwindled, and then, perhaps by now a little tired, might haul onto the rough concrete slab opposite the main viewing gallery. But there was no question of rest for Rondo during the hours when people had paid to watch her; no possibility of the sleep she would have taken in the wild when The Ages told her it was time. Should she lie too long, inactive on her slab, she would be tempted off with a piece of fish or prodded with a long pole until she took to the pool, sleep and humour denied her to satisfy greed and the publics' ignorance.

There were other such centres around the country, but well run, where the welfare of the animals in care was a priority and where efforts were made to find out more about them and to do everything to ensure they were kept in surroundings as close as possible to those they knew in the wild. Much of the money taken in was ploughed back into new facilities, and they were places, too, where the public could be educated and put in touch with the creatures they had come to see. But this was not to be Rondo's lot.

★   ★   ★

It had taken her until early spring fully to recover from the plague. Others had been less fortunate, and despite the dedication of people like the woman who ran the sanctuary, many had died. It had been none of the seal's doing, nor that of any fish or the smallest creatures of the ocean upon which all others ultimately depend. The lodges of cod and conger, the hunting grounds and spawning rivers of Leaper and Tail Shaker had not been fouled, never been pillaged by their

own Kind; only by the hand of man had such things been
done. Men thought that they were guided by clever heads,
but all had been powerless to prevent the spread of seal
plague. Governments had blamed other governments, large
corporations blamed their competitors, and the people; the
people blamed them both and, too, the people of other cul-
tures, other societies. Those same people had elected the
first, spent fortunes on the products of the second without
knowing what they contained, and rushed to beat the last
with the superiority of their own economic power without a
single thought of any long term consequence.

For those such as the deerstalker of Loch Shielside, the
new hope which had begun to spread as seal plague faded
was no more than a thief, robbing the public of the reality of
what he saw happening in the world. His wife chided him
and called him a pessimist, but he would hear none of it, her
admonitions serving only to make him think even more
deeply and vindicating his growing conviction that there had
been more to seal plague than appeared in the press. The
two vets who had come to collect Rondo and her mother's
body had been guarded, but after a time had admitted there
might be wider implications. To someone like the stalker it
was no more than common sense that if a creature's food
became polluted over a long period then that creature itself
would absorb those pollutants. This was true not only in the
case of seals but of every living thing on the planet. The same
rule of thumb applied to all things, and in any food chain
such as that where seals were at the highest level, or those of
bears or wolves or the red deer on Dun Mountain, then the
more poisons absorbed throughout the chain, the more that
the chain itself, through its individual parts, lost its integrity
and its inherent strength.

To him it followed that, the weaker a food chain became,
the more that parts of it were liable to succumb to sickness
or even catastrophic diseases such as seal plague. Speaking
to his wife he likened these things to the unnatural practice
of feeding cattle with manufactured products containing
their own offal, such as brains, hearts, kidneys and the like.
The powerful giants of the industrial world who had

pioneered these practises had promised accelerated growth through the use of these products, but why on earth, argued the stalker, should we think that we could feed meat to an animal which had spent the last five million years evolving into a beast so perfectly adapted to eating grass! The cow has even grown itself an extra stomach just to cope with it, he ranted. And how could they continue to pour filth into the sea all over the world and then tell us that things like seal plague have nothing to do with it? These people were supposed to be clever. These people had strings of academic qualifications. Somebody had better draw up a university course in common sense he thought, while there was still some of the planet left that hadn't been completely wrecked. His wife shook her head in mock despair and smiled. Her husband was becoming more and more irascible as he approached retirement, and though at times she found the change in him amusing it tended to unsettle her for he was far from stupid and had never talked anything other than good sense. Maybe he had a point.

Perhaps it was with these things in mind that she kept in close touch with Rondo's progress at the sanctuary, phoning the woman every week for news. She had been pleased when Rondo was considered well enough to be moved to the marine centre, but something held her from expressing too much enthusiasm, something she could not explain and which the woman of the sanctuary found slightly disquieting. When asked if anything was worrying her, the stalker's wife was hesitant and merely muttered a few words, saying that things usually turned out for the best and she hoped the pup wouldn't be too upset by the journey. The matter was set aside, and the stalker and his wife busied themselves with the routine of their lives.

★　　★　　★

Rondo had been made drowsy for the journey by the sanctuary's vet, and had arrived, a little confused but in good spirits. The voices had been different, and the pup immediately began to miss the company of the seals she had come to know at the sanctuary. She was well looked after and well fed, but after only a few days began to be bored with her dull surroundings and the lack of company of her own Kind. Days turned to weeks and Rondo began to show the physical results of being enclosed. The chemicals in the water, put there to keep the pool free from bacteria and fungus, acted on her skin, causing large tufts of her coat to fall out, leaving in places pink sores which took a long time to heal. Her days were meaningless, dull and empty, enlivened only at feeding times which she became able to anticipate almost to the minute.

Frustration came more and more often, especially when the breeze blew in sea smells she knew must have come from no great distance because of their strength. The ocean lay only thirty seal's lengths from her pool but it might have been a million. The Ages told her of the sea's proximity, and although, in the quiet of evening when visitors had gone she could lie, listening to its surge and longing for its freedom, depths, distances and the limitless space of it, all Rondo could do was eat what she was given and explore, again and again, the dull, rectangular, concrete walls of her prison. Her muscles were losing their suppleness for there were no tides to swim against and no hunting grounds where she might lunge and twist, speeding after conger or Tail Shaker with every muscle keened to what her good eye saw and what the Message of The Ages told her of her quarry. Where once she knew no boundaries, no horizons or controls, now her feeding, her vision and movement, her sleep and wakefulness, every part of her life, all were out of her control, she was powerless and could do nothing to help herself.

Her muscles wasting, her mind dulled and with her spirit already waning, Rondo, as she approached the anniversary of her birth was no longer a beast of wild places; no more a living mirror of The Ages work, but nor yet was she one of man's animals, evolved over centuries to domesticity and with few wants but food and water.

★   ★   ★

Towards midsummer, as the surviving seals of Loch Shiel turned their thoughts to Birthing Rock, the stalker's wife received a call from the woman at the seal sanctuary. She had followed the seal's progress, and her alarm had grown, she said, as the men who ran the marine centre failed time and again to release Rondo. She had travelled to the centre to see for herself whether the reasons they gave for the delay held any substance or, as she had begun to believe, were merely excuses. When she saw Rondo swimming aimlessly, alone in her dull, sterile pool, she had at first felt pity for the animal, then shame; shame that she had in some way failed the seal, that she had taken less care than she should in securing the imprisoned beast's release and had spent less time than necessary in checking out the two men and their backgrounds. She had seen other marine centres and what could be achieved in them. Many of the other seals she had cared for had gone to places like those. Why, she thought, had she not made greater efforts to find Rondo a place in one of them, perhaps one closer to the Northlands from which she could have been released after a few extra weeks of care.

When she confronted the two men and demanded to know when Rondo was to be set free, at first they had mumbled more excuses then, seeing she was not convinced, became rude and abusive. They told her that the seal was their responsibility now, their property, and it was none of her business if or when the animal was to be freed. The woman had seen the numbers watching Rondo before making herself known. She had seen the hundreds of cars and tour buses in the car park. It didn't require a genius to assess the sums of money being made, and the woman demanded to know whether it was their intention to release the seal or merely to use it to make money for themselves. They walked away, refusing to say more.

She had left the place in tears, saddened and full of her own, undeserved shame. But much later, after she arrived home and had time to think, sadness and disappointment turned to anger: a bright, controlled flame which she was determined would burn until the seal was returned to the wild. She would not be thwarted. The dedication, patience and determination she and others had shown through years of work and care at sanctuaries such as her own had been adulterated by men who had done nothing to help any stricken beast during the time of the plague. Now, cynically, they had turned one of her charges into a cash register while she and her like still struggled to make ends meet, never concerned about their own pockets but only for the creatures in their care. She knew that, above anything, she had to put things right.

The stalker's wife was horrified when told the story. The sanctuary owner asked for their support, but when she talked of the press it was clear there was no way the couple could become involved, for the stalker's boss, the owner of the large estate on which he worked, wouldn't be pleased if an employee spoke to the newspapers. He was a city business-man who spent only a few weeks of the year in the Northlands and was not interested in matters such as broken promises unless the deed had been done to himself. He expected his servants to take the same view, and if the stalker or his wife had spoken publicly about the one-eyed pup it was likely he would lose his job. With it would go the house they lived in, and despite his rare and long learned skills, any chance of similar employment in his home area would be out of the question. All they had would go, and strongly as they both felt, the couple knew they could not afford to take the risk.

But the stalker's wife, after much thought, found a way round the problem. She had a niece, who had spent many happy summers on Loch Shielside and was now a journalist in a southern city. She was not known to her husband's employer, but to be doubly safe it was agreed that the niece should hand the matter to a colleague. Over the next two weeks the marine centre where Rondo was being held was visited by a number of people who, without making them-selves known, counted the numbers of visitors and made an accurate assessment of how much money was being made out of the seal's plight.

The owners of the centre were confronted once again, this time by journalists with tape recorders and cameras. Their justification for keeping Rondo was, they said, because with only one good eye she would be unable to hunt and feed herself properly. She would soon die if released so it was better for her to be kept there, well fed and well looked after. When it was put to the men that there were many known cases of seals surviving with similar injuries, even instances of completely blind seals living for years in the wild, otherwise fit and happy, they could say only that Rondo had been in captivity too long now to remember anything she had learned as a pup; they were experts they said; they knew what they were talking about: they would not try to tell the press how to run a newspaper so the press should leave them to look after the seal.

Newspapers and television channels picked up the story. It was public property. They featured the seal sanctuary and all the hard work the woman had done over the years, but this time, unlike on previous occasions she had been featured, she asked for money for every interview. She was not prepared to take prisoners in her fight against the marine centre, she said. It was all or nothing. There had been no written undertaking, she agreed, but the seal would not have been given to the men on any condition other than that it had to be released as soon as it was fit enough. It had been done, she said, in exactly the same way her other seals had been sent to other centres all over the country, with one single purpose: their release into the wild after the shortest possible time. The men at the centre insinuated that the woman had accepted money for Rondo, but this only served to anger her even more and drove her to double her efforts, speaking to all who would listen, confident, assured and knowledgeable, not self righteous, but very obviously right. The men were forced to apologise for what they had said, wishing privately that the woman would have a nasty accident or even die.

The public began to demand that the authorities act, but they were powerless. A number of organizations threatened court action against the marine centre but this was fraught with problems. Who, for instance, was an expert and who wasn't? Who did one listen to? Nothing was done, and as time rolled by, the more publicity the centre received, the more the customers rolled up to the turnstiles: rather than being set free, Rondo was now making more money than ever by courtesy of a tasteless, vulgar public. The owners had real reason to be grateful to the woman of the sanctuary, and now joked about sending her flowers and a letter of thanks.

But the attitudes of some had already hardened, particularly of those on the fringes of a small number of organizations who are always ready to exploit an opportunity, to gain a supposed, moral advantage over the rest of society from some situation, regardless of how it is achieved. Threats were received at the centre and the owners became frightened and quickly realised that their days of easy money were numbered. In the meantime, guard dogs were brought in, huge brutes with ugly, wide heads and jaws like steam presses. More than the weight of a man and an insult to all the Ways of The Ages, they had been bred for one, single purpose; to imbue fear in any would-be intruder. Icons of the impoverished minds of men, these symbols of terror became the guardians of a defenceless young seal, these and a high, barbed fence, standing between Rondo One-Eye and freedom.

★   ★   ★

The pool drained slowly, noiselessly. It was the middle of the night and Rondo had been asleep, floating on her back rather than hauled onto the featureless, concrete slab. As the water ran out, her body had sensed the change and she had wakened. She looked below, then sank the remaining few seal's lengths to the bottom, trying to work out what was happening. Knowing the level had dropped she swam towards her hauling out slab but found it too high out of the water now to heave herself onto, and she knew also there was insufficient depth for her to take a run at it from below and drive upwards from the surface. Soon she was only half afloat, her belly rubbing on the bottom and her fear growing as she realised the pool was almost empty and she had nowhere to go. She heard scuffling above and began to panic, her heart racing and her good eye focussing on where her ears and nose told her the disturbance was coming from. She turned to face the noise. A ladder was being lowered over the edge of the pool. She saw the first, human shape begin to descend and took fright, shuffling noisily around the pool looking for some means of escape. Then, as two figures approached she stood her ground, twisting to face them, spitting, her teeth bared, ready once again to fight for her life.

Not for the first time in her short existence she felt something being thrown over her then pulled loosely round her head to prevent her seeing anything or biting. She felt herself being bundled, fully conscious this time, not fighting for breath and half drowned as in the fishermens' net, and not as she had been when the stalker rescued her from Whale Rock, sick, full of the poisons of seal plague, This time she was aware of every frightening, confusing sound and each strange, uncomfortable movement. She was terrified, and though she rebelled with all her strength and spirit she was completely powerless to do anything.

She was hanging in the air now, swinging from side to side, her body bent inside the tarpaulin which held her fast. She was bumped and scraped, not painfully, but adding to the grip of fear and shock that was overtaking her senses. There were low voices, and by The Ages she sensed urgency and desperation in them. Her fear continued rising and adrenalin raced through her. As she felt herself being landed on something solid she emptied her bowels and bladder simultaneously, making her hidden handlers curse loudly as the mess spilled onto their hands and arms.

Half carried, half dragged and by almost now frozen with fear, the pup felt herself being moved again. After a short time, and above the stink of her canvas straitjacket there came a different smell, more familiar, almost friendly: and there was a rushing sound which, despite her confusion, she knew must be the sea. The voices quickened. She knew she was lying on stones for she could feel them through the canvas which now seemed less tight around her. There were chinks of light, too, and she could move her head, so lashed out with bared teeth aiming for anything within range. There was an angry shout and a boot was driven into her side, winding her and numbing her into stillness. She felt herself being rolled over; the canvas had gone: there were no more voices, no sight or sound of men, only the seas surge close to her. She had been released. At last, Rondo One-Eye was free.

The newspapers were full of the seal's disappearance. It was quite clear she must have been set free, but nobody knew who had done it. There were more questions than answers, for the dogs which roamed the centre each night had been let out and had wandered the streets of the nearby town. The local dog catcher and the police who had great difficulty in catching the brutes, couldn't help wondering how those who had cut through the wire had managed to escape injury from the dogs. The centre's owners blamed animal rights activists, but those groups denied any involvement, saying that it was equally possible that their accusers were responsible, that the episode might be no more than a cynical means of saving face. How, they asked, had the pool been emptied so efficiently? But the owners said that anyone with basic knowledge could have done such a thing, even by just spending a few days at the centre and watching how the system worked.

Of Rondo there had been no trace, and speculation as to her fate played a major part in almost every point and counter-point made. The owners of the centre said she was certain to perish, if indeed, she wasn't already dead, and that she was totally imprinted on humans, meaning that she depended entirely on them for food and wouldn't know how to feed herself. Others disagreed, saying there were numerous cases where animals had survived in the wild after much longer periods in captivity. Reports appeared in the press of one-eyed seals being seen in various places around the coast, but there was nothing definite, no photographs and nothing that could be corroborated.

The story lost impetus as other, more immediate matters took the attention of the public. Without Rondo the marine centre declined. The supply of coaches trickled and other travellers no longer came for miles to see the one-eyed seal.

When finally it closed its tall, barbed gates for ever, few regretted its passing.

★   ★   ★

There had been no sound but the sea surging onto the stones below her. She looked around at the dark night, not realising what had happened, not knowing yet that she was free and could take to the water and feel its wide, boundless welcome. She shuffled round, calmer now and with her senses beginning to revive, receiving messages about her surroundings from smells and sounds. For the first time in half a year there were no glaring lights shining down on her, and she took in every glimmer from sea and sky, collating, interpreting, trying to merge the messages to find one single answer. Slowly she began to move, hesitant at first as though unsure of what lay ahead and watching already for the unseen or unheard. The stones were rough, but their slippery, weed-covering helped Rondo's progress to the water. On the very edge of the ocean she stopped. Raising her head, and with a glimmer of moonlight catching the rough edge of her shrivelled, left eye, she sniffed long and deep at the sea smell, hissing as she expelled her breath. The Ages cautioned her. She looked over the water for long seconds before moving down the last few lengths to rest for a moment, half submerged, but already beginning to feel the sea's caress.

Still not quite knowing she was free to go where she wanted, perhaps expecting the end wall of her small pool suddenly to appear and stop her, the seal moved forward hesitantly. Sliding ahead across the stones and weed until fully afloat she swam slowly into deeper water, looking downwards through the darkness, her eye focussing on what lay below. She was not sure what was happening, whether she was free or if this was some trick. She rested on the surface, now looking up to the stars, her nostrils wide. Messages were coursing in her mind trying hard to cut through the confusion which surrounded her. Suddenly, almost as if she had seen some vision, the one-eyed seal made a slashing, half-turn and dived with a splash that could have been heard even from the viewing gallery above her pool. She submerged, seeking the bottom in a long, shallow dive before levelling, rising again and powering seaward, the taste of freedom driving her.

She had been swimming directly outwards from the beach, her course not varying by more than a degree. After about ten minutes she slowed, then stopped and turned to look back at the shore. Although the sea was almost glassy calm, a long, low swell ran in from the Atlantic, and when in the troughs between high, billowing swells her view was cut out save for thirty seal's lengths or so around her. But when lifted by a crest the whole coast was picked out by twinkling lights, among them the powerful floodlights of her awful prison of so many, miserable months. Gradually her breath and heart rate slowed. There were no men, no faces looking down from the gallery, no noise save for the ocean; no cackling or shrieking of human voices. There were no lights over her, bright burning, their awful intensity keeping her from sleep, and above all there were no walls or barriers, only the vast, unending wilderness that is the sea. The seal looked round, feeling with every minute more and more relaxed, more at home. She was tired, but there was no rough, concrete slab on which to haul out. With a last glance beneath the sea and a long look towards the lights, she rolled on her back and let her tail drop so she floated almost vertically in the water. Rondo slept the quiet sleep of freedom. No dreams were in her head that first, free night: her sleep was deep and peaceful. The moon dropped behind thin clouds and even as the haze of a pleasant summer dawn made its way across the eastern sky, still Rondo slept.

★   ★   ★

Perhaps because it arrived so gradually and slowly, the noise did not disturb Rondo until it had become very loud and its source very close. It was like the sound of a wild, rain-filled river coursing across rocks into a Northland loch, and the seal half woke as The Ages wrote the memory of Rough River in full spate across her mind. But as she looked round,

searching for the familiar sights of Bay of Shelters or Dun
Mountain, what faced her then was nothing she had ever
seen before.

The Ages had no name or Message for the monster that
bore down on her. All at once the huge beast blotted out the
newly risen sun and Rondo barely glimpsed the white,
foaming bone which hung between its teeth before finding
herself swept before it. A great roaring was in her head and
she closed off her ears, trying desperately to find a way to
escape the tide which was hurling rather than carrying her,
tumbling her over and over as the beast grew ever closer. She
rolled and saw its full height, rearing seventy, eighty seal's
lengths above her, rising and falling slowly in the long swell.
The boiling foam was almost on her, the noise, the vibration, all numbed her senses, but still, as confusion coursed
through her mind she fought, twisting, writhing and turning
to find some purchase in the foam, driving with every ounce
of power she could find. The noise was deafening, flooding
every sense until the seal could no longer think or reason.
She was blinded, deafened: and there was not the power in
such a small body against such a giant foe.

And then, almost as quickly as it had arrived and over-
powered her, the beast set her free. Rondo had been cast
aside and the great ship sailed on. Dazed, she broke surface
in its wake, the noise of its huge, powerful propeller still
thrumming in her head as she looked up to the stern to see
the heads of four men looking down from the poop deck and
pointing towards her. She did not dive, knowing the beast
was travelling away, but swam clear of the turbulence of its
wake and watched the ship disappear towards the west. She
looked around for some familiar sign but there was nothing.
The coastline was to her north; there would be feeding there.
She had felt hunger and knew already that she must hunt.
She had not forgotten, and the first and most important part
of Rondo's next battle for survival was already won. She
swam north-west towards the land.

By mid-morning a shimmering haze had spread across the
sea towards the western approaches and the Atlantic. There
was little breeze save that which trickled from the continent

to the south and Rondo recognised none of its smells. She swam purposefully, and though still confused was wary of the many boats and ships she could see from the surface and hear when she dived. A few miles ahead, rocks and cliffs gleamed in the sun in pale, soft colours, but without the familiar backdrop of dark hills of her homeland. Her hunger growing she looked around under the surface almost as though expecting to find mackerel or herring thrown there by her keepers. She drew closer to the coast and saw now its rocky nature and the long ground swell surging from the ocean, breaking in surf over weathered stone. Upright in the water with her head high she eyed the shoreline, searching for any small stretch of beach or a slab on which she could haul out. The whole seaboard was exposed to the ocean here and there were no small headlands to turn and dissipate the swell with sheltered bays behind where seals could haul out safely. Her confidence was not enough that she felt she could hunt in safety until she had found some sort of haven, no matter how small or tenuous, so despite the hunger she felt, she continued on her unknowing way.

All day she swam steadily along the coast. Throughout the afternoon strange tides tugged at her, forcing her to move in or out from the line of cliffs to find slacker water which would not impede her, but then, as evening closed, the tide turned, sweeping her slowly westwards and allowing her to rest and watch. A moon had risen, tall and yellow in a sky that stretched unbroken towards the west, and Rondo's eye was pinned to that moon for she had sensed a change. She had begun once more to heed The Messages of The Ages; to think again in the way of her Kind and, as she noticed the almost imperceptible change in the moon's angle, she knew that the direction of the tide's flow had shifted. There had been no slackening, only a change in direction to the north, carrying her closer to the shore. She moved with it, knowing somehow of a need for greater speed, but swimming easily, confidently and as if with insight, watching always, carefully judging her distance from the shore. The stream began to swirl and eddy, changing speed and direction every fifty seal's lengths or so. She was much closer now and the cliffs stood tall in the sky above her, hiding the moon so only its pale glow could be seen. There was excitement in the seal, for she seemed to know by The Ages of some confluence ahead, some joining not merely of waters but of senses; of Messages and signs. She looked northward. The view was opening and with every westward seal's length the northern sky became more and more unbroken by land. The swirling currents eased and the flow, though still towards the west, became steadier and less swift.

At length she was carried through a stretch of broken water where short, steep standing waves foamed and fought against each other, contrasting with the calm sea around them. As she cleared the rougher patch she looked north and saw the sky, unbroken now between the heavens and the moonlit sea. Rondo looked hard, and perhaps sensing that this could be her seaway home, she swam towards the head-land and the gap to its west that appeared to leave her north-ward passage clear. The exhilaration of her journey had left her tired and hunger gnawed hard in her belly. To the north of the high outcrop the weather was calm, and she made her way inshore carefully, searching as she swam, knowing already that she would find a place to rest. She hauled onto a steep, gravel beach and pulled herself above the highest level the flood could reach, knowing, too, that escape would be quick from such a steep place. Once in her chosen place she turned to face the sea and looked out, checking for any-thing which might be a danger. Within ten minutes she was asleep, fourteen months old, almost to the hour.

Chapter 16

It was some days before the stalker and his wife heard news of Rondo's escape. He held out little hope for the seal given all the circumstances, but, to him, the whole episode had come to represent much more than simply the troubles of a sick animal. He would retire in another two years after a life spent working among the rich variety of moor and mountain. He had seen many things and come to understand most of them. He had seen sickness in bird and beast but never anything like the disease that had decimated the seals. Often in the past he had felt amusement when warnings about the modern ways of man had been sounded on television or in the press, for he lived in a pure, clean place where the sea was bright and the running water in his house came, untreated, straight from a spring on the hill behind. But things were changing. Perhaps he had always known it, he thought, but had put it to the back of his mind not wishing to spoil the great contentment he felt and his good fortune in having a stable life and a loving family. Could it be that he might be at least partially to blame for the sickness that had overtaken Rondo's Kind and some of the other ailments of the planet? Was the rest of all humanity really at fault when he, with his own special insights had said nothing? Would anyone have listened if he had?

On the afternoon they learned of the escape he and his wife had sat talking in their small garden. Summer was all but over, but Dun Mountain still basked above them in late sunshine. They talked of the changes they had seen over the many decades they had been together and how the place might change even more in future. The stalker had been born in that very house, and all his happiest memories were tied to it in some way. He felt a surging of anger, for he had come to see that all the smallest changes had coalesced to alter land and sea, to change the planet irreversibly. The seals had been but the most recent casualty of the hand of man. What might be next? The deer on the hill; Talon who sat above them now on Dun Mountain? Perhaps the year was coming when they would not see or hear the sights and sounds which signalled the seasons, the first swallow or October's cry of geese as they arrived from Greenland as they had done since before man came to live on Loch Shielside. And then, even man himself might reap the harvest he had sewn, his own Kind dying in hundreds of thousands as had the seals. It might be no bad thing for other living things were that to happen. But what could they do, two of them among so many? Perhaps it was as well to treat each day, each sight or sound as though it were the last, to watch the eagle or the fox as though they would be gone tomorrow, forever, struck out by the hand of man. Across Loch Shiel, above the ancient pines of Sword Island a raven circled, calling to the dusk. The stalker shivered, and turning to look at the wife he loved so dearly, saw tears in her eyes.

★   ★   ★

For over a week Rondo stayed close to the beach where she had first hauled out after rounding the headland. It was a safe place, isolated, protected on three sides by high, steep cliffs and accessible to men only by sea. Her weight had fallen, for some of the fat she had developed during the months in captivity had metabolised and was being used to replace energy as she began again to learn the ways of her Kind. Hunting below the steep cliffs, she had spent long hours searching and chasing in vain before her suppleness returned and she began to find success. Luckily she had come across a broad mud bed where large red prawns found food in the debris washed in by the tides. Rondo had remembered her days before the plague and hung motionless, just she had done in Loch Shiel, hiding close to a boulder then dashing out to take what she could. With every hour of hunting, speed and agility returned, slowly developing towards a level where she could be assured of food. She met few other seals, for many had perished here during the worse days of the plague and those she encountered she was wary of. None had joined her on the narrow beach, though an ancient cow of Gerda's Kind had lain several times in the shallows without hauling out.

Days were shortening and the wind turned more often to the north-west, chilling Rondo as it blew directly onto the beach. By The Ages, from the relative positions of sun and moon she knew a time of big tides was coming, and these, if joined by gales from the north-west might strand her, their combined power making her unable to gain the safety of open water as high, green rollers raced onto the beach, pounding all in their path against its rocky edges and the cliffs behind. She knew she must move soon to another place, sheltered and near which she could find food enough to continue building her strength.

One night the old cow of Gerda's Kind hauled high onto the beach, close to Rondo. The younger seal spoke in her own tongue and raised a flipper towards the cow, signalling that she would not be moved and would fight to retain her place on the gravel. The cow ignored her, turning after she had hauled high enough to look out over the peaceful sea. Rondo watched her for a while. Rondo sensed that the old cow was not resting, and though relaxed, the beast was attentive; almost as though expecting something to happen. She kept lifting her head, gazing steadily towards the ocean. The beach was steep and with the tide as low as it was now the seals had the advantage of a long view, something denied to them at surface level. Rondo kept watching the cow. There was a good moon, not too bright, and the sea, being calm didn't make moonbeams dance but gave instead a steady, clear glow.

The cow straightened her neck. She had seen something, Rondo knew it but had no inkling of what it might be: food, danger, another seal, perhaps. She watched as the cow slithered purposefully down the beach and followed her wake as she swam outwards. Something was strange: the sea was calm but there was something out there. Something was dancing, glinting; a wide circle of shimmering beams seemed to be below the surface. The Message of The Ages was in Rondo, and within seconds she was moving towards the ocean without fully knowing why. Diving now, her one eye turned forward seizing every smallest gleam of light and uniting all to form the only image of importance at that single time, in that one place, for ahead of Rondo One-Eye was a shoal counted not in hundreds nor in thousands but by the thousand score, – mackerel, known in the Northlands as one of the three great spirits of the sea.

In her haste Rondo didn't notice the grey cow swimming below her. She was watching, judging distances and preparing to gain the best benefit from the least amount of work. But she had seen the yearling and waited, knowing that her work might be done for her. Rondo approached the shoal in a straight line from a few seals' lengths below the surface. She powered towards them, every ounce of muscle working at full pitch.

The shoal was ahead of her, bell shaped in the water and shimmering in continuous movement. As she entered the mass of fish at full power, believing she was about to take her first bite, it split in a smooth, harmonic wave, leaving a void around the seal so that whichever way she turned and no matter how quickly, the mackerel were protected by the empty zone and able to remain outwith her striking distance. Increasingly frustrated and using energy to no effect, the seal chased around inside the shoal. More by luck than judgement she caught one fish which by chance had been displaced from the main movement. She rose to the surface to draw breath and eat her hard won prize and then, refreshed, dropped slowly through the water to relocate the shoal and try again.

The Grey seal had by this time eaten three good mackerel. She had taken full advantage of Rondo's youth, moving almost casually to the bottom of the shoal as the yearling first dashed in from above, cutting out a small number of fish which then lost confidence by being separated from the main body of the shoal. Singled out in such a way, a small group would become erratic, and single fish could be cut out and pursued using learned skills rather than raw energy.

As Rondo sank again she began to watch the Grey cow. She would separate a dozen or so fish from the main shoal, then, after pursuing them lazily for a short time, speed into the side of the group, twisting and snapping, her old, wise eyes watching for the first to break ranks. The pup followed, tracing every move until at last she was able to jerk to one side and take a fish that had thought itself safe, She swallowed it whole then took another as it tried to regain the safety of the shoal and was panicked into swimming almost straight upwards: an easy kill.

Both seals rested under the moonlight. Rondo was tired from her exertion but felt the benefit of eight, fat mackerel in her belly. The old cow, ever wise, waited to see if her new companion was about to make another foray, but the young seal was happy to wait until the older beast began to hunt again. After some time the cow took to the depths once more, followed eagerly by Rondo. An hour later they were back on the narrow strand, replete and at rest. Rondo had eaten more that evening than in the last three days.

The mackerel on which the two seals were to gorge for the following few weeks had fattened all summer far to the north. They were dependent on the movement of other, smaller fish for their own sustenance, and life for them was an endless cycle of finding, fattening, travelling and searching then fattening again. Their yearly journey had varied little in the past, but now the small fish they fed upon were more scarce and difficult to find in the old places, making the mackerel look to other, more distant waters in order to survive where the fine meshed nets of men had not plundered everything. The mackerel, too, suffered in nets, and their shoals had been depleted to a fraction of what they had been only twenty years ago. Now, fishermen who had before always known where and when mackerel would arrive in a given area were puzzled when the fish failed to turn up, it being beyond the wit of men ever to apportion blame to himself for anything that takes place in the natural world,

even when the time of fishes on the planet measures in decades against the few seconds since man first stood on two legs.

No matter that the shoals were not the size they had once been, for the present the two seals were content to keep in touch with the fish as they came and went. The grey cow knew their ways and was patient, and with the weather beginning to worsen, on the seventh day of the feasting she left the open beach and hauled out, followed by the pup, in a small, sheltered cove where the sea was turned by a steep headland. When hunger called the cow she would cruise to where she seemed to know the mackerel would arrive, and though she and Rondo were not of the same Kind, the lessons of The Ages were in them both, so each benefited in some way by the other's presence.

★　　★　　★

At this time of year most of the grey cow's Kind were giving birth, then mating. She herself had passed the age of bearing pups and was living out her life in peace, feeding and resting as she liked, an opportunist, aged and experienced. Rondo gained confidence and strengthened. She grew more patient, too, when faced with the vast shoals, and waited like the grey cow, picking the best moment to strike. She began no longer to follow the cow at all times for her senses had sharpened and her one eye keened swiftly to the quicksilver of a shoal whether she was above or below the surface.

The days continued to shorten as winter grew close; the weather became colder and at times it was wiser to sleep at sea than in the cove where wind-chill stole so much heat from the seals that even more fish had to be caught to replace it. After a few weeks of harvesting the two seals found themselves hunting further and further afield yet making contact with the mackerel shoals less often. An increasing number of journeys were being wasted. Then, they were gone altogether, and with them went Rondo's teacher.

For a few days after the last shoal had gone Rondo hunted aimlessly, close to the shore near her cove. She had fattened nicely and was now stronger and fitter than she had been before the plague. As it grew ever colder she spent more and more time in the water, for the cove became difficult to enter at times as winds whipped up tall, confused seas and the currents swirled. At midday on each successive day the sun was lower. The evening light faded earlier, and though this did not affect the amount of food the seal found, somehow it made her feel exposed, as though she should be in some more sheltered place; but she knew nothing outside the small area where she had hunted the mackerel shoals, and of no single beach where she would find safety and shelter. Rondo knew that she must move, where she did not know, but she must pick her time, heeding The Ages and travelling with care.

One night as she rested at sea the seal was carried offshore by the current and woke to see no sign of the coast. There was nothing familiar in the tide flow and neither could she find any landmark she recognised below the sea. The moon was low and barely visible through the cloud, but a few stars broke through the haze and as she looked around, her good eye focussing on the infinity of the heavens, lessons learned since the days of The Seal Fathers came to her. The Message of The Ages turned and pointed her. Without thinking more, Rondo swam slowly northwards.

Chapter 17

For two days she saw no land. Swimming easily or drifting in shallow sleep, Rondo was carried northward, and into that part of the sea between the Southlands, from where she had come, and a Green Isle to the west. On the fourth morning dawn broke to show a high island to the north under a cap of straggling, white cloud. Rondo quickened; hunger had not touched her yet but she had travelled far and felt the need to lie up, secure on some slab or beach to dry out, scratch and clean her coat. She closed with the island's coast searching all the time, taking in the ways of tide and current and watching for boats and other seals, anything which might bear on her safety or progress. She sensed the wind, too, knowing she must find a place with a good lee if she was to be safe from wind chill and breaking seas.

After finding herself a small meal, Rondo came upon a long, rugged skerry on the island's western side and separated from it by about a hundred seal's lengths. She looked carefully at the rocky islet for the sky was angry and high clouds travelled fast. Satisfied she could haul out there as high as she needed to escape wind and sea she began to search the seabed, for there were still questions she must answer. Were there hidden dangers such as sharp, cutting rocks which could damage a beast? Was there food? It served nothing if she would have to travel miles in search of fish.

She swam slowly down the seaward side of the outcrop, keeping just above the jumble of rock and weed of the bottom and searching methodically in every likely place. On the inside, between the islet and the main island, was a kelp bed, its roots embedded in a long, narrow strip of rock.

Among its fronds were many small fish, and in the mud and sand around it were prawns, crabs and flatfish. Rondo nosed around using her long whiskers to explore narrow places and the thickest of the weed. She heard, too, the sounds of other seals, signalling their greetings as they swam some distance from her. At length she was satisfied. There was food enough and shelter here to keep her at least as long as she needed to rest. She surfaced, and within an hour was asleep above the highest mark of the tide.

Over the next few days she remained close to her new skerry, venturing no more than half a mile to either side. Then, for almost a week, fierce gales lashed the area and Rondo was forced to sit tight, hunting when she could during any brief respite, but since she knew no other place more sheltered, always remaining close to her refuge. The weather calmed as a ridge of high pressure took hold, and although it became very cold the wind no longer drove spray high on rocks and beaches. The sea became completely calm, a stretch of dark, burnished glass rippled only occasionally by light cat's-paws of breeze. Rondo fed well, seeking out new grounds, searching banks and caves and always learning.

Her resting rock was sometimes shared by another seal, a male of her own Kind who had three summers. They roamed together, working as a team, just as she had done a few weeks previously with the old, grey cow. Among the kelp or on the more open, boulder-strewn ground that lay further offshore there were cod and whiting, all mainly in small shoals and each Kind with its different Ways. The two seals maintained their weight throughout the fine weather, and when at last it broke and coasts were lashed with storms again, they rested without hunger.

After a few weeks, on a morning when a sudden gale had prevented the two seals hauling out as they returned from hunting, Rondo followed the male as he made his way to the north side of the island where he knew he would find shelter. They had made an easy passage, searching each bay for any chance of food as they travelled. Rondo had inadvertently surfaced close to a small fishing boat, into which two men were hauling lobster pots. It was her closest sight of human faces since she had been freed and she dived suddenly in fright, but one of the men had seen her clearly and told his companion he thought it must have been the seal all the fuss had been about on television and in the papers. The other laughed, saying that the distance between the place where the one-eyed seal had disappeared and where they were fishing now was too great for a seal to have travelled, but the other argued she might be making her way back to the Northlands where, he was sure, she had been captured. The memory of the faces stayed with Rondo throughout the day. It had frightened her, for there were scars in her mind as well as over her eye. Later, as she and her companion rounded a point and the male had swum directly towards a small harbour with boats and men plainly visible, Rondo hesitated then turned away and swam to a ledge under a tall cliff where she hauled up out of sight and rested uneasily until the wind dropped. After a few days she returned to her skerry in the west, but there was no sign of her companion so once more she had to hunt alone.

The weather turned even colder as under clear skies a steady wind blew out of the north. Rondo remained sheltered from the worst chill but was uneasy. Fish were becoming harder to find and recently the tides had become strong and unpredictable. The young bull had not returned, and other seals, although around, came no closer than a few dozen lengths from her resting rock. She dozed in the cold air, trying to make up her mind whether she would be warmer in the water than on her skerry, for with food so hard to come by, energy was at a premium and difficult to replace even in small quantities without using her precious reserves. She slept well for a while but woke in darkness to find herself even colder. There was a change; something was different. Rondo was facing south and shuffled quickly to her right, her mind quickening. Pillars of light appeared to spring from sea to sky; flashing columns of colour lit the heavens and turned the sea to a silver gauze as the aurora rang out in a silent anthem. A Message called. Rondo slid into the water, and swam towards the lights.

★   ★   ★

The young seal was exhausted for she had swum many miles, ever northward. She had eaten little and for what she had taken had dived deeper and for longer than ever before. Rest was out of the question, for the westerly wind which only an hour before had been a light breeze was now blowing hard. There was no ocean swell, but heavy seas were building, beginning to break in foam as they crested and rolled towards the distant land, and angry clouds obscured the sun for all but the briefest glimpses. Rondo kept her direction, knowing by The Ages where the land lay. Even at her best speed she was more than five hours from the coast and her passage north would be lessened with every increase in the wind as she was swept eastward in the welter of sea and foam. She struggled on, knowing she could at least stop swimming and just let things happen, allowing herself to be swept at the sea's wish; but that in itself held dangers, for it would mean that she herself was not in control, and when a landfall was finally made, or at least its proximity sensed, she may find herself unable to reach the shore safely. Such disasters, slow in the making, are often swift and sure in their ending.

For what seemed like days the seal was carried by vagaries of wind and tide, first this way and then another, though her general path continued to be northward. A great swell, larger than any Rondo had seen before, built from the west, and she knew by The Ages that in that direction must lie the open ocean. The wind dropped and the sea soon lost its crashing power leaving only the billows of the swell. In the Atlantic, a great storm, the strongest for many years and one which had taken the lives of many creatures, had just passed, and the swell was its tired but still powerful aftermath. With the calm, the seal, at least when carried to the smooth, flat crest of each swell, was able to keep a look-out, and no longer allowed herself simply to be carried, but swam slowly towards the north-east where she knew she would find land. Occasionally she dived, hunting desultorily in the deeps, realising that anything she took would be by chance alone. She saw few ships but made sure she kept well clear: seals there were, too, grey beasts of Gerda's Kind which, as she went ever north and east, increased in number until there came a point after which she saw no more.

The sun had all but disappeared into its red and yellow haze when she saw the long, low shape of the island. She stopped to look, craning her head at the top of each swell and trying to make out if what she saw was really land or only a straggle of dark cloud close to the horizon. She was tired and hungry. The Ages spoke to her and she swam hard, her direction straight, unerring and filled with purpose. She approached the island's coast to feel a swirl of ocean as it met with coastal currents, and suddenly there were other seals, many of them, all of her own Kind. She slowed, taking stock of her surroundings. There seemed to be two islands separated by a narrow sound. The one she was closest to, the southernmost, seemed the larger but flatter of the two. Rondo kept well offshore. It was nearly dark, but there were too many seals and in her tired, hungry state she would not risk a fight by barging onto another's resting rock; she must find somewhere on her own; peace to rest and regain her strength before hunting in the morning and exploring this new place.

There were no lights, nothing which spoke of man or other dangers and the sea was calm. At the first gravel beach she found she tried to haul out but was defeated by the swell, so turned back and entered the sound that separated the islands which, because it was so narrow, dissipated the billows, calming the ocean, though never quite taming it. After a short search she found a small outcrop, empty of seals and sheltered enough should the wind rise from any direction other than the east. She swam round, taking care despite her weariness, sensing the tide and checking everything she could find. At last, satisfied, under a clear sky she hauled out and fell quickly asleep.

She woke several times that night, scratching and cleaning herself on each occasion, for it had been days since she had dried out properly and her coat was full of lice and other seaborne parasites. After each cleaning she lay awake for a while, looking and listening, watchful of any danger which might come suddenly upon her. But there was nothing to cause her disquiet, no noise or lights or boats, only the smooth waters of the narrow sound and the stars of the clear, northern sky. The winter night was long and the sun rose late in the morning, but sensing the direction from which it rose, by all the other things she saw around her, the taste of the sea and the smell of the air, Rondo, though in a strange place, knew she was no stranger there. She had arrived. She had come home to the Northlands.

Chapter 18

On Loch Shielside, changes were happening both on land and in the water. A few years before, foreign trees had been planted which grew quickly, becoming thick and green, blanketing the ground and cutting out all light from the thin, peaty soil they clung to. Deep furrows had been ploughed to drain the ground in preparation and the trees then planted on the ridges between. The soil now drained much more quickly than had been the natural way of things, but the companies who planted these thick forests had taken no account of the effect any of this might have on Rough River; that its levels, its very chemistry, would alter drastically through the increased drainage of the newly planted slopes which fed the ancient streams: that the river might die, slowly but certainly. Leaper and Tail Shaker might still mount Rough River's falls to lie at rest, waiting, lying deep in holding pools until The Ages called them to spawn in the redds of its headwater, but, over time their numbers would decrease, for the eggs they left would be swept away in greater and greater numbers, as in periods of heavy rain hillsides drained ever more quickly causing catastrophic, flash floods. But the few, fragile eggs which did survive still had to hatch, and the young fish spend a year or more in Rough River before making their way to the ocean to grow and make the muscle which would allow them to return to their birth streams when Glen Scent called them. The Ways and Messages of The Ages would prove unable to cope with such speed of change: Leaper and Tail Shaker were doomed now, more surely than if all the pillaging by men and the worst ravages of disease were visited upon their Kind.

The stalker and his wife had watched all these things. In the beginning, he himself had believed them to represent progress rather than impending doom. The trees, it had been said, would bring prosperity, create employment and revitalise the most depressed parts of the Northlands. No matter that they destroyed the land. No matter that they would kill the ancient stream of Rough River and all her stock, or that the promised jobs were yet another myth. The real reason, the underlying motivation for these plantations may well have been prosperity, but it was not the prosperity of the people of the Northlands but those who were already rich, the favoured few whose writ was money and who, in return for their investment in such forests, were given benefits which far outweighed the value of these foreign, devastating trees. Once again, and with Harvester's promises to The Messenger long forgotten, the hand of man was busied to destroy yet more of those things wrought by The Ages. How long, the stalker wondered, would it be until the world could stand no more. In his own time perhaps, even with his life's work among the hills and on the moors he loved so much almost complete. And now there was a new concern, for with catches of Leaper and Tail Shaker decreasing yearly and their price rising in accord, the clean pure waters of the Northlands had been put to work; the salmon farmers had found Loch Shiel, and with these men, as with the foresters and their trees in the Glen of Rough River, was power enough to forge irrevocable change.

They, too, had come with promises of jobs; a new dawning of prosperity with a new, burgeoning industry, ideal for the small communities of the Northlands. The jobs came, and with them, for a time at least, there came a measure of prosperity.

But the jobs that were taken up so eagerly were not ones which involved decisions or policy, for those were occupied by servants of the corporations which had brought the fish farms there. Giants, monoliths of international industry whose decisions, always, are based on global considerations, never the greater good of any single, small part of any country. And movement on a global scale was a simple matter for these companies, so that if conditions altered in one part of the world, if the waters they farmed became so heavily polluted with the detritus their overstocking created that an operation became no longer viable, without apology or explanation it was simply closed down and the business transferred to some other part of the planet that had, so far, escaped the hand of man. These companies employed clever scientists whose success in breeding fish had been spectacular, yet few of them had knowledge of those things where nature has the greatest say. Few of them knew anything of the places and communities in which they found themselves at work, and those with reservations about any aspect of their jobs kept quiet, or were fired. Their industry was entirely market driven and numbers were important. The Leapers were kept in cages in deep sea lochs like Loch Shiel, where, fed on the pulverised guts and bones of their already harvested and processed fellows, the fish grew fast.

At first there were only a few places where cages could be seen, but as science allowed the fish to grow more and more quickly and prices fell, demand grew for more and more Leapers, and in a relatively short time there were few of the great sea lochs of the Northlands where cages were not in evidence. Local people had little or no say in where they were put, and inshore fishermen found their sheltered, winter fishing grounds covered by vast spreads of cages. Governments stood back, fearful that if they attempted to control the industry the companies involved would pull out.

*   *   *

With every full turn of the sun there are two tides in the Northlands, and in the normal way of things it may take a thousand tides to flush completely a body of water like Loch Shiel and carry to the ocean all that has been put there by the hand of man and by bird and beast and blade. In this way The Ages clears the debris of nature, and all that live in such places are only so many as will ensure their hunting grounds are not fouled by the excessive waste of their own numbers, which would bring dearth, disease and ultimate extinction. It is the same for all things; for the Kind of Talon of Dun Mountain; for Rondo's Kind, for Leaper and Tail Shaker: for man himself.

The salmon cages of Loch Shiel were filled with young fish; hundreds of thousands of them; many more than would ever have been there without man's interference and more by far than the natural flushing action of the loch could cope with. They were fed whatever mixture was fashionable in the industry at any time. Invariably, this contained parts of the bodies not only of their own Kind but of others such as pigs. Their feed was spiked with even more unnatural substances, such as dyes to turn their flesh pink, a colour it could not take naturally without their normal diet of wild, arctic shrimp. The fish emptied their bowels continuously, and the waste fell to the loch bottom where it mixed with the remnants of uneaten food, dyes and medicines, turning a once pure, clean place into a fecund breeding ground for scavengers and parasites which multiplied ten thousand fold beyond The Ages' plan.

Because of the great mass of water in which they had to be effective, huge quantities of fungicides and antibiotics were used in order to keep the fish free of disease, but despite this, sickness was more or less endemic from the beginning, for the fish had not the openness of oceans in which to move, no room to dart or dive, to learn of speed, pursuit; escape: all the lessons required by The Ages. If one fish caught some infection or disease, such was their continuous proximity to each other that the ailment would spread like wildfire. As filth built below their cages and populations of parasites burgeoned, disease and sickness became the norm, creating havoc with stocks, spreading through the water like dye through a wash, infecting and killing wild Leapers and Tail Shakers as readily as their captive cousins. Then, even more medicines were used. Antibiotics and anti-fungal preparations were thrown at the stocks of captive fish, and the detritus of those preparations washed in and out with the tide before sinking slowly through the water column to the bottom, touching everything, corrupting every balance of The Ages, damaging all but the most basic or resistant organisms which lived there. In almost every way, the Northlands was undergoing deep and fundamental change, all wrought, solely, by the hand of man.

Chapter 19

The sun was bright, but it was low and winter-weak. Pale light flooded across The Sound, and Rondo, awake and hungry, looked around to take a first, daylight view of her new surroundings. She scratched again, stretching a fore flipper high over her back in search of some microscopic annoyance. She felt lazy, still tired from her long, fraught journey, but knew by The Ages she must explore and hunt to keep her energy reserves at a high level, for it was not the time of herring or Tail Shaker and she must take whatever she could find. She looked down to the water a few seal's lengths below where she lay and knew the tide was at the beginning of its ebb. It would be an hour before its strength had built enough to restrict her. She took to the sea and dived.

The small outcrop where she had slept was one of many. Where The Sound flowed into the open sea at the eastern side of the two islands there were scattered at least a hundred such islets, all of them, when the weather was from the western side of the compass, ideal resting rocks for seals and all manner of birds. That morning, despite the numbers of her Kind she had encountered on her arrival, there were no seals in evidence. She hunted, and soon came across a muddy bank which looked as if it might yield a meal. She took some small dabs, pushing them from the mud by moving her head from side to side and using her nose as a sort of plough, catching them easily as they tried to escape. The water was clear and shallow, scattered with kelp covered reefs, sandbanks and in places, huge boulders. These she used as cover, either to spy the ground ahead by lying tight against the rock or by using them as blinds, swimming at speed directly towards them in a straight line then swerving round, ready to catch anything which lurked on the other side. From time to time she surfaced to draw breath, on each occasion taking care to relate what was below her to what she could see of the islands, The Sound and its reefs from above, all in the same way as a man will take his bearings from street names or buildings in a strange city. In such ways she would be able to return with ease to this place should she find nowhere better to feed.

For about an hour she explored, taking all the food she could find. It was little enough, but went some small way to restoring the energy she had lost on her journey. She kept to the areas around the rocks, not yet venturing towards either of the main islands and expecting soon to feel the tide's pull as it strengthened, a signal for her to return to the outcrop where she had spent the night and on which she knew was safe. As the tide gathered pace she drifted lazily, allowing the flow to take her and keeping her head underwater much of the time, watching below for anything of interest. She did not haul up, but lay where she first touched, for the tide would drop away beneath her and there was little point in using energy and making work when The Ages would complete the task at no expense. Though it would be dusk before the water rose again she knew she would launch and hunt before the afternoon was out, searching for more clues to help bring her sustenance, seeking out new resting places, dangers and escape routes. Should she stay in this place for long, the seal would spend many hours in such pursuits, gaining local knowledge before she could count on a real margin of safety in her existence, all in the Way of The Ages.

Two hours before low water Rondo slid from the rock and swam into The Sound. The tide was now stronger at the shallower edges so she kept to the deep channel which ran east to west and stayed slightly closer to the rocky, northern island than to its flatter partner to the south. At its narrowest point The Sound was no more than a hundred and fifty seal's lengths across, and here, when there were storms coupled with big tides, the channel could become a maelstrom, and fishermen from the islands feared the place in foul weather for in past years many had gone to their deaths there. As The Sound widened on the west side Rondo sensed the water becoming deeper and dived steeply to see what lay below. The shelving was steep, rocky and hung with a thousand Kinds of sea plants, waving as they danced to the ocean's surge. Rondo slowed, searching in crevices and among the fronds, but found little that would feed her, for here, on the border between coastal water and ocean the ground was scoured continuously by the force of the Atlantic and little save the hardiest creatures could survive. There were strange, tugging currents there on the exposed edge and the weak, winter light penetrated no more than a few seal's lengths below the surface. Rondo did not tarry, for the sun was already low. She rose to the surface and looked around. Both Islands were visible, but the northernmost seemed somehow more attractive and she swam back towards it, following the line of the shelf until it ran oceanwards and she had to turn in towards the shallows.

There were more rocky islets here than on the eastern side where she had spent the night but still no sign of the seals she had seen last evening. Small creeks punctuated the coastline and she searched each one, picking up a few small bites of lumpfish and dark, rock codling. It was enough. Relaxed though ever watchful, she spent little energy in all this, learning more with every length she swam. She had reached a point where the land swung eastwards and she could see to the north where, in the distance, a number of other islands, some with tall mountaintops, were scattered. All a seal could see from such a distance was a blur, but Rondo sensed the presence of these places and stared hard towards them even as the tide pulled, telling her to return to safety. Once back on her reef she preened in the dying light, scratching lazily as the red glow over Northisle faded. For the first time since she had been taken from Loch Shiel, Rondo One-Eye felt some small contentment.

★   ★   ★

A single hilltop dominated North Isle beneath which lay a small loch fed by the streams and runners of the hill and its surrounding moors. A tumbling, narrow river ran from the loch, first south and then to the east around the foot of the hill, greeting the ocean with a short, vertical waterfall beside the island's only village. A narrow, curving creek ran some distance eastward from the fall, and there the boats of fishermen were moored, safe from wind and sea. From August until late September a great gathering of Tail Shakers would run into the creek when darkness joined a high tide, and if there had been rain enough to swell the stream they would ascend the falls and make upriver to the loch without halting. If prevented from running the falls by lack of water they returned to sea with the ebb, swimming close to the coastline until the next spate came when they could try again. As rain fell and the river rose, carrying Glen Scent to the sea, the fish became more and more active until at last, in frenzied effort, they were able to gain the pools above the falls. Until that ascent could be made the fish were forced to remain in open water, and seals and islanders harvested them.

There were times of year, too, when shoals of mackerel and of herring skirted the island, sometimes even passing between the treeless skerries and the shore. Then, as with the Tail Shakers, islanders harvested, seals gorged and nursing cows made milk in plenty for rapidly growing pups. All these things happened in a place which all creatures felt was safe and, above all, clean and clear, washed as it was by the great Atlantic.

There were the normal dangers to a seal's existence. There were Eye-Peckers of course, though not too many, for they attacked the islanders' young lambs and were shot regularly to keep their numbers down. The seals were never bothered by the people of the Island, and even those beasts which swam right into the township creek to play or hunt near the falls were not shouted at, stoned or shot, for the islanders were of an old race, tolerant and, still superstitious of beasts they viewed as knowing of their own ways. The only real danger to the seals from men was from the fishermen who

came from time to time from other parts and laid out their
trammel nets in long lines. But, all in all, the island was a
place of peace. There was none of man's forestry, only the
few windswept trees which grew there naturally, clinging to
any crevice in the rock. Apart from the islanders' livestock,
every other creature there had grown and flourished in the
manner of The Ages, and in the main was unaffected by the
hand of man. To the people who lived there it was a place of
beauty and tranquillity where they lived in harmony with
bird and beast and blade, all things having their own part to
play in a much greater scheme.

The island's seals, unlike those of Loch Shiel, did not
choose one particular place as a Birthing Rock, for there
were countless small islets and skerries and shelter was never
far away. There were, too, few human visitors to the island
compared to the hordes who visited the mainland every
summer, and pups were not in danger of being found, sup-
posedly abandoned, and removed by city dwellers, or to
suffer a similar fate to Rondo's at the hands of Puffin's crew.
Those visitors who did venture there, so far off the beaten
track, were likely to understand the ways of bird and beast
and leave all well alone. For the new pups then, there was
security, and the multitude of skerries, bays and sandy inlets
were an ideal playground for young seals, the rich variety of
feeding to be found among them ensuring that the skills
demanded by The Ages were well learned at an early age.

The two islands were milestones in the lives of many
things, for they stood alone, not close enough to the mainland to be considered part of it, nor part of the long chain of
islands which formed the islands that men call the Outer
Hebrides. During the migrations of spring and autumn they
were visited by thousands of birds, resting on their travels,
northwards in spring, and, in the shortening days of the last
glimmering of summer, south to Africa to escape winter
storms and darkness. Whale and dolphin knew these islands,
for their surrounding waters had always provided them with
food and shelter, a welcome resting place from the vastness
of open ocean. There was a feel about the place, a sensing by
all things, including its people, that it was essentially of

nature, virtually untouched by those things which spoiled and corrupted so much else in the world. In such a place was Rondo One-Eye fortunate enough to find herself, and there, in that quiet corner of the earth was her best chance of growing and becoming strong, and of finding her place in the complex society of her Kind.

Winter was close and the air was full of the cries of geese as they arrived from Greenland and the Arctic to spend the winter along the western seaboard until the first, soft, south winds of early spring called them again to the far north. Rondo stayed on her quiet skerry for several days without venturing again through The Sound. Other seals passed as she lay at rest or hunted close to her rock and became used to her, and she, in turn, began to recognise the most regular visitors. Conventions were not broken and the Laws of The Ages were satisfied.

Chapter 20

Despite the pain and confusion that had typified so much of Rondo's experience, it now stood her in good stead, for she was more circumspect, more suspicious of what appeared strange or beyond her knowledge than many seals twice her age. This did not mean she wasn't inquisitive, but in calculating risk, as every bird and beast must do throughout its life, Rondo took her time, preferring to wait rather than to blunder in. On any occasion when she slipped from this useful habit, as she had done when the mackerel shoals appeared by the island on her journey north, she quickly realised the futility of excessive speed. Better far to watch, and, if possible, to learn from another, older beast. So, in the short days Rondo began to find her place, slowly, without urgency but still managing to find all she needed to fill her belly for the days of winter.

The winter solstice was only half a moon away but the weather had remained settled so the numbers of seals passing Rondo's skerry remained steady and she was able to recognise a growing number. A few of the island's boats, too, fished nearby, and the men who hauled their heavy lobster creels payed scant attention to the odd seal that happened to be about. Rondo came to know the regular boats. She could hear the thrum of their engines as they turned the corner from Creekharbour to the open sea. Their different sounds and tones became familiar, and quite soon the seal knew that the crews of these boats meant her no harm. Still, she kept her distance, and on hearing an unknown engine or propeller kept well out of the way until she was sure she was safe and could return to her skerry. Once or twice, curious as to where the boats went after they had disappeared, Rondo had swum slowly and carefully into the creek, but so far had ventured only to where the entrance narrowed and turned. From there she had been able to see part of the Village and a number of boats sitting peacefully on their moorings in the space below the low waterfall. She had not felt it wise to go further, but more, valuable knowledge of her surroundings had been gained, and when next she was near the creek she would go further.

At the north end of Northisle, a few miles from where the river ran from its falls in to Creekharbour, was a small, almost completely enclosed bay. The narrow channel which formed its entrance turned in its course through ninety degrees, and when the tide was at its lowest was no more than five seal's lengths across and deep enough to accommodate only the smallest boats. Where the channel widened as it met the sea it was dotted with many, small rocks and skerries, some of which were completely covered at high tide, making it a dangerous place for boats without local knowledge. There were a few larger islets, two of which were the same size as Sword Island in Loch Shiel and gave shelter to the smaller rocks inside them at the channel mouth. It was among this tangle of reefs that most of Northisle's seals made their homes.

In heavy weather, a seal swimming landwards from the sea to the inner bay had to exercise great care if it were not to be pounded on the many, partially submerged rocks. First, it would pass between the two, larger islands, then surface and take a line towards a huge splinter of rock which hung over the channel entrance. Following that line, the beast would turn only when within a few seal's lengths of the crag and make along the sandy trench of the channel until it opened into the bay. From there the white beach at its head was revealed, surmounted by two grassy fields above which stood a small dwelling and a half-ruined cattle shed. The bay itself was fairly deep, being a good four seal's lengths even at the lowest tides, and its bottom of sand and mud made good holding ground for the anchors of the few yachts that visited in summer. The house above the beach was no longer permanently occupied. For as long as anyone could remember it had been part of the croft, or smallholding on which it stood, but the family to which it had belonged had died out, and now, having been sold for a high price because of its location, it was the holiday home of a well off family who lived far to the south in another country and came there for only two or three weeks in every year. To the seals of Northbay it made little difference whether the dwelling was occupied or not, for the old crofting family had never bothered them and the new people, for all the time they were there, were more a diversion than a nuisance as they called and whistled, trying to attract the beasts onto the beach.

On the same side as the overhanging crag at the entrance to the channel, short, steep cliffs ringed the bay all of the way round to the edge of the beach at its head. Opposite, the land lay lower close to the tideline, almost as though the cliff slabs of the other side had been tipped over to form long, sloping haul outs which the seals used in the worst northerly gales when the shelter of Outer Bay was lost. From these slabs a seal was in full view of the small house and could see the rising, narrow ribbon of track which led south to the village. It was the most peaceful part of the whole island.

From the rocks of Outer Bay the seals could watch over a wide arc of the surrounding sea, particularly the reefs to the east of the two, larger islets. From there, they could see and hear the movement of seabirds, whales and dolphins, and all these things gave them information which, though rarely vital on its own, added to the sum of their knowledge about the endless movement of shoaling fish.

The seals noted the passing of all other sea creatures; whales, dolphins and, the vast, lethargic basking sharks which came in schools of a dozen or so and fed only on plankton. There were, too, unwelcome visitors, and though these came mostly in human form, the one which struck real fear into the minds of seals and left them nervous and unsettled for days, was Orca, the killer whale. If a school passed, catching Rondo's Kind unawares, the devastation could be terrible, leaving the Northbay colony much depleted. When it was known among the seals that Orcas were nearby there would be a great fuss of noise and thrashing of water with heads and flippers before all hauled as far above the highest tideline as possible. There would be grunting and hissing and spitting, so that any seal making in to the land with its head above water would be warned of danger and make haste. Such visits were rare and impossible to predict, so the seals of Northbay had constantly to be on their guard. In many other areas, such as close to the mainland coast, seals were little bothered by the Orcas, though in those places there might be less ground on which they could feed and less variety, so the beasts were much more dependent on the movement of migratory fish such as Leaper or herring. It was a price all paid in some way, constant danger in return for diversity and openness, shelter and safety in exchange for occasional hunger.

In any season, when high pressure brought stillness to the weather and turned the sea to shimmering, blue glass, seals from Northbay ranged far around both North and South Isles. Depending on the time of year, some preferred the wild and rocky seaward side, where the Atlantic surge was never stilled and swells rolled even at the calmest times, smooth and lazy over the weed strewn rocks of the shore. There, in deep water beyond the zone where the surf scoured everything, beneath current and counter current and among dense forests of sea-wrack and kelp were the lodges of many creatures, and though a seal had to work hard against the pulls and tows of the swell's backwash, the rewards to be gained repaid the effort, for stocks of sea creatures there were largely untouched by men's nets. The seals were well served by the sea and what it provided, and like those of Loch Shiel were a community which grew or contracted according to season and weather. Now, at midwinter, the beasts were more widespread, ranging further than the close environs of Northbay to find food, sometimes remaining away for days as they hunted and finding some small islet on which to rest as Rondo had done when she had arrived.

*   *   *

When she had been on her skerry near The Sound for about two weeks, after hunting one afternoon on the western side, Rondo had returned to find for the first time another seal hauled out and asleep on her favourite part of the rock. Making no attempt at a direct approach until she had some knowledge of the stranger, she circled, coming closer to the animal with each pass. All she knew of the beast was that it was a bull of her own Kind. She reached the shoreline a few seal's lengths from the him and lay, half submerged, watching for signs. The stranger woke and looked lazily at Rondo, greeting her in their own tongue and giving no sign that he was annoyed at being disturbed by a younger, smaller beast. Rondo returned his greeting and hauled out carefully below him. He was in her favoured place but she would not risk a confrontation by trying to push in too close. She was still wary, nervous, for although the bull appeared friendly he would not necessarily remain so for long. She turned and looked out to sea, feigning confidence by preening and cleaning her coat, all the time peering back towards her elder whose main interest now was only in more sleep. After some time, when Rondo realised she was in no danger of a squabble she began to relax, and with her belly full, dozed in thin sunlight as the tide fell back from the skerry.

When she woke she had forgotten the bull behind her and looked up in surprise as she heard him move. He greeted her once again and she replied, relaxing immediately as she sensed peace in his sounds. He moved down towards the water and halted, looking round. He scratched himself, then, with a single heave launched the remaining half length into the sea. Rondo watched as the bull cruised round the islet. Something spoke to her. Something unfathomable told her to follow the stranger and she, too, slid into the water, swimming easily in his wake as he turned and made off to the north.

The two passed the entrance to Creekharbour, and from there the ground over which they travelled was foreign to Rondo, for she had never ventured so far. Nonetheless, she continued to follow, though ready at any moment to turn south to the places she already knew. They moved on the surface, both animals taking frequent, long glances below, and at times diving several seal's lengths, the better to see some strange or unusual feature which might be worth remembering. The bull's interest was mainly in trapping any food which might appear along the way, and Rondo, too, would take any such opportunity. On one occasion she lost track of her new companion and almost turned back until he reappeared behind her, fresh from the pursuit of a large eel that had escaped into a crevice almost as the bull's jaws closed around it. He ignored the yearling, going at his own speed and in his own way, never giving Rondo so much as a glance. To him she was merely another incident, part of everyday life. As The Ages had decreed, he, as any other seal, felt no responsibility for her. He would warn of danger, but only because danger to one was danger to all; he would do no more or less than that, his duty to their Kind, as had been done since the days of The Seal Fathers. That she followed him was her own responsibility and her own risk, for only in such ways can bird or beast learn the lessons of The Ages. The light was fading as the two seals arrived among the tangle of skerries on the eastern side of the entrance to Northbay. The bull dived and swam a seal's length below the surface following his favourite channel among the rocks and beds of kelp and wrack until close to the two, larger islets where the main channel entered from the north. He surfaced and looked around.

His favoured resting rock there was occupied by half a dozen seals, but he hauled out low on the islet, knowing that the tide would soon fall away beneath him. Rondo was unsure. She had not ventured into this place before and never had she been in the company of so many seals, for there were at least forty scattered around the reefs and rocks and she remained on the surface, looking around in the half-light for an empty rock. There were none and she began to turn, ready to make the long journey back to her safe skerry beside The Sound; but something held her. She searched again; there was a gap on one of the smaller reefs, a rough place which others had ignored in favour of flatter, smoother slabs. She swam towards it, slightly nervous but in an odd

way, assured, as though her hard experience might keep her
safe. She passed no greetings to any beast. She had no wish
to stand out among these strangers, wanting only to rest and
then be gone. Risk was implicit in what she, a stranger, had
done by hauling there, and she had to reduce that risk as
much as she could. It is not always the strongest which
survive, but those best able to weigh the odds, reduce the
chance of even the smallest argument which, among the
Kind of man so often leads to war or ruin.

For an hour or two the darkness was complete, but then
the sky cleared and the true coldness of winter could be seen
in Northbay, a brittle, bitter cold under a sparkling, star
filled sky. A freezing mist formed which seared the throats of
bird and beast as they breathed, keeping them from the most
restful depths of sleep, and as night passed slowly, on reefs
and islets the seals huddled closer together, seeking warmth
from each others' forms. Rondo moved slowly upward on
the rock as other beasts moved closer to each other and
made more space available, so by the time the tide had risen
to full height, the one-eyed beast was at the edge of a tightly
packed group, her nervousness allayed by the common need
of all for warmth and the desire for sleep.

Most were awake before the late, winter dawning. A few
took off almost immediately for their hunting grounds
which, at this time of year, might be some distance away, but
most remained, waiting for weak sunlight to bring a small
warming and rid them of the frost which showed like a light
dusting of snow on their coats. Rondo stayed where she was,
not wishing to move and risk causing a disturbance. One or
two beasts had already sniffed softly at her, taking her scent
so they would know her again, and one, a youngish cow, had
greeted her, remembering Rondo from recent days when she
had hunted by The Sound.

The young seal took a first, clear look at her surroundings,
scanning every feature with her head tilted in what was now
her signature, the odd pose by which she could be marked
among her Kind. The view from Northbay was quite different from everything she had become used to on the skerry
further south, for few other creatures had shared that

territory. Here, it was almost as though she were in a new land, for all manner of birds and beasts were there: goosander, cormorant and eider shared rock and water with the seals, and within a few lengths of them, some of the island's deer grazed in the winter morning. Although all these creatures lived together more closely than any others Rondo had yet come across, Northbay seemed neither busy nor noisy. There was plenty of activity, but all was done in the way of The Ages, and apart from the occasional squabble between seals, life was led at an easy, quiet pace. Despite Rondo's natural wariness, something about the place seemed right to her. She had been greeted so far only by one other seal, but as the light grew and movement among creatures increased she knew there were others there she had seen before. The bull with whom she had travelled was on his resting rock sixty seal's lengths away, where by guile and experience, he had found his way to the best, most comfortable spot, and on another, small reef much closer to her was a young cow she had met near The Sound, who she greeted gently in the tongue of seals.

Rondo shook herself sending a spray of frost into the cold air. She scratched, using the claws of her front limbs to comb her coat, cleaning it of weed and parasites picked up on her journey the evening before. Well fed after her weeks beside The Sound she could afford a day or so without food as she explored, but for the present was content to stay where she was and bask in the small warmth of the sun, watching carefully, taking in everything which could be of use to her. She watched the roe deer, the first she had seen, as they grazed peacefully in the field below the house, which, though no longer under cultivation had not yet become overgrown with bracken and still managed to give the roe a thin supply of winter feed.

With the sun at half height Rondo began to slide to the tideline in stages, checking the bay and its surroundings each time she stopped. She felt no urgency for any activity, for in the Way of The Ages she knew by now that she would remain there among the others of her Kind, and swam idly among the islets, content for the present to explore just as

the mood took her. Her confidence grew as she passed reefs
where seals lay basking, either ignoring her or merely sniffing as she went on her way. She searched the channels, but
as yet did not venture through the narrow gut to the inner
bay and its beach, some of which was hidden from a seal's,
surface view except at the highest point of the tide. But it
would not be long before she had explored every last part of
Northbay and its surroundings and the deeps which lay on
its northern side. Not long either before she settled into the
routine of the colony, mixing with others of her own age and
learning from those with the knowledge of greater years.

★   ★   ★

The solstice passed and was followed by a period of
strong, north winds which sent seals and seabirds to the
inner part of Northbay for shelter. On the islands to the
north, snow capped the high peaks which shone red as the
sun rose and set. The chill of winter was deep in the earth of
the Northlands and for all creatures it was a time of waiting.

Among the seals at Northbay, at this time of year there
was no real sense of territory so far as hauling out space was
concerned. They rested where they could, and though many,
particularly older animals, had favoured places to suit the
wind or weather of the day, it was seldom that disagreement
disturbed the peace of that quiet corner. After a few days
Rondo began to settle among the extended family of the
colony. She had made no real effort to get to know any other
beast, preferring to remain inconspicuous, and when she had
come to know another more closely it had been as a result of
coincidence, rather than any deliberate attempt to befriend.

Sometimes, a seal might prefer to hunt on its own, but
there were times when it was better to join with others, especially when shoaling fish were in the area. When working
together like this, a stranger such as Rondo would come to
know the strengths and weaknesses of individuals more
quickly; what each was best at, whether standing sentry on
the edges or at shocking, fierce pursuit, for as with the Kind
of man, a team needed a variety of skills if it were to succeed.

The time of snowmelt approached and days began to stretch. Rondo had explored most of the east side of the island and at times had returned to her old resting rock by The Sound to spend a few days hunting in the places she had found after her arrival from the south. On one occasion she had been forced to swim home to Northbay exposed to the occean's edge along the western side of the island when a fierce, east wind had risen suddenly and played havoc with tides and currents making her resting rock by The Sound untenable and a passage home on the Creekharbour side too dangerous. She was in fear then, for the wind could have carried her far out to sea, and because of the interminable ocean swell which pounded the seaward shore in winter, even in an easterly gale she could not afford to swim too close to the island, or she could be caught in the surge and smashed to her death on unforgiving rocks. It had been a severe test, and in the way of The Ages, one that she had passed only in so much as she had stayed alive. As the first, spring warmth reached the birds and seals of Northbay, it seemed that Rondo had begun once more to thrive.

With longer days came warmth and settled weather. With growing confidence, Rondo moved farther afield and explored almost every creek and corner of the island. Like the others, she seldom went south of The Sound to the low, flat land there with its shoals and banks, but hunted round the rocky shores of Northisle and on the great bank off its northern coast. In Creekharbour, the one-eyed seal had been seen playing under the falls by a number of villagers. The story had spread and became known even to the stalker and his wife on Loch Shielside, who wondered if it could be the same beast they had known. As the anniversary of her escape approached, a few stories appeared in newspapers, and holiday-makers to Northisle who had read them searched hard for sight of Rondo.

Even before they had disembarked from the small ferry which ran from the mainland to the small pier outside Creekharbour, visitors quizzed bemused crewmen about the one-eyed beast, and were told wild, unlikely stories of the seal's supposed exploits, which most of them believed.

Northbay became busier than normal as cyclists and walkers visited the place, and when the family from the far south arrived for their yearly holiday at their summer house, they became annoyed by the intrusions of these extra people and locked the gate where the road dropped from the hill down to the bay. The fuss soon died away, and the seals, in any case, had been little bothered, happy enough to remain on the reefs of Outer Bay when too many people were about. The season's pups were growing and there was food in plenty all around. Only a few yachts had visited Northbay that summer, picking their way slowly through the channel, watched by seals and birds, and anchoring below the old house and its two fields. On one had come a man who at once fell in love with the place and wanted it more than any other thing he had ever seen. He was a man used to having what he wanted.

The summer had been dry, but in August, as shoals of Tail Shaker circled the isle waiting to run the falls at Creekharbour, the weather changed drastically. Day after day, black, water-laden clouds drove landwards from the Atlantic, emptying their rain across all the islands of the west and the mountains of the mainland coast. The hill above Northbay was a myriad of runners, all feeding the stream that ran over the beach, until it became so fierce as to cut a wide channel in the sand. Swift and muddy, it ran into the inner bay carrying Glenscent to fool Leaper and Tail Shaker into thinking it may be their home river, and Rondo and the other seals gorged as the confused fish made bid after bid to run the stream at each high tide. The owners of the cottage watched the seals chase the frightened, leaping fish, trapping them by blockading the narrow gut at the entrance. Even the youngest of that season's pups joined the feast; learning, growing fleet and supple with the chase.

In the same way as the seals feasted, so, too, did every smallest form of life below the surface of Northbay, for as the seals ate, skin and bone and flesh was dropped and fell through the water column to be taken by the likes of crabs and smaller fish. As they themselves ate, more again was spilled and so the whole food chain enjoyed the scrapings of the seal's table and in turn, thrived and enriched the sea's floor.

As rain teemed onto the land the people in the house grew bored. Their children, used to city things, grew fractious and complained incessantly that there was nothing to do. All of them remained indoors out of reach of a sodden paradise. Before the passing of ten moons, the dwelling would be sold.

Throughout the late summer and autumn foul weather continued to lash the Northlands, and rivers ran in full spate for weeks on end. Leaper and Tail Shaker ran in and spawned quickly, many making their escape back to the sea almost as soon as spawn was down among the stones. By the end of that wet season Rondo had learned fully to cope with the disability of having only a single eye, and as the winter Solstice approached once more she entered her last six moons as a juvenile. By next midsummer, if all went well, she would be ready to mate.

Chapter 21

Lambs began bawling for their mothers and the alarm calls of small birds rang around the fields beside the house. Seals looked up and peered through the narrow gut as the noise continued, some taking to the water and swimming cautiously to Inner Bay to investigate the cause of the disturbance. Near the house was a large vehicle from which three men were unloading equipment and carrying it to the half-ruined cattle shed at the rear. When the truck was empty the men left, driving slowly up the hill and stopping to lock the gate. The birds and beasts of Northbay returned to the routine of the day.

In late afternoon the men returned and unloaded more equipment. Again the lambs cried out and once more the seals went to investigate and watch as the men worked. When they had finished they walked through the small fields on the east side of the beach, each carrying a large sheaf of papers. All three stood above the entrance gut, looking at the papers and pointing in all directions as they talked. Lights shone that night from the cottage, the first since late last summer.

Early next morning the sound of voices carried through the stillness to all the rocks and islets of Outer Bay. Lambs began bleating and birds, unused to such disturbance at this time when they had already begun to nest, sounded their alarms above field and shore. The men had a large, rubber boat which they inflated then left above the highest tideline. They separated and went across the fields and around the slabs and rocks of the entrance to the bay carrying rods and posts which they stuck into the ground in various places.

Cormorant and eider moved quietly away as they pro-
gressed, and the seals, too, grew wary and moved out to the
farthest reefs, even though the men ignored all but what they
were doing. There was much shouting and signalling, stakes
and posts were moved around and instruments were used to
measure levels and gradients. Only after the sun had reached
its zenith did the men stop, sitting quietly in front of the
house to eat.

The noise of lambs and birds died away as the men took
their break. When they rose to continue their work it began
again, though not in such volume as before, and this time the
seals didn't bother to swim in to Inner Bay, by now knowing
all they needed. But when they heard the spluttering of a
boat engine, all raised their heads in alarm. All eyes were
fixed on the channel, every animal was poised for flight as
the rubber boat made its way noisily through the gut. As it
came into view some took to the water, sliding or rolling
rapidly from their resting places and diving immediately,
heading for the outer channel from where they could make
an easy escape. Others, older beasts, less wasteful of energy,
remained, waiting to see what the intruders might do.

The tide was almost at its highest. The men had pots of
paint, and on a number of the large rocks which remained
visible above the water on either side of the channel they
splashed large, white marks. As they completed the first two
or three reefs near the narrow entrance to Inner Bay, the seals
that had remained hauled up watched carefully, not moving
yet, but as the boat began to point directly towards the two
main islets, all of them took to the water almost in a single
move, leaving every rock bare of beasts and the surface dotted
with heads, all watching the invasion of their territory.

The process was lengthy for the men had to take care not to
damage the rubber boat, and before they began to make their
way back to Inner Bay the tide had already turned. Slowly, the
seals moved back to their rocks and hauled out, carefully
avoiding those places which were now covered with the stinking, white substance none had seen or smelled before. All
creatures were unsettled, their routines and feeding cycles
broken, and even after the men had disappeared into the

house and silence returned, all remained watchful and nervous.

The intruders remained two more days. The boat was not used again but the men scrambled over the headlands on each side of the gut, shouting to each other as they used instruments to measure even more levels and distances. On the day they left, bird and beast watched indifferently as the van and trailer were loaded. After the gate had been locked and the last hum of the engine died behind the hill which led southward to the ferry, the creatures of Northbay began to settle quickly into their old routine. After a few days, it would seem to all of them as though nothing had happened.

No bird or beast could know it, but the men had been the harbingers of what was to happen soon to the place where all had lived in peace since the ice had gone. The cottage and its surrounding land had changed hands; bought by the wealthy yachtsman who had visited Northbay the previous summer and wanted to own the place. He was not prepared to spend such a large sum without return so would build holiday houses, second homes for the wealthy, on the land around the cottage, to defray his costs. The channel into Northbay would be marked; a jetty was to be built and yacht moorings laid in Inner Bay. Some of the seals' resting rocks obstructed the proposed channel, so it was planned to blast them out of the way with gelignite. Water and fuel would be provided for visiting yachts and all these things would help pay for the man's purchase and enhance the new resort's future value. No native person would be consulted, for such is the way that land can be owned in the Northlands that only two people owned almost every part of Northisle; the rich yachtsman from the south who had bought Northbay, and another, a banker who lived in another country. Although the law would not allow the small farmers and fishermen who were tenants to be put out of their dwellings and livings, the owners had no need to consult them about any development, and only their councilmen who lived on the mainland could do anything to stop what was being planned for Northbay. The lessons of the history of the Northlands already indicated that they would do nothing to prevent it.

It was also a time of coming change for some of Northbay's seals, for as in every year, a number of cows of three or four summers would mate for the first time, bearing their calves twelve moons later. As days lengthened and the time of pupping drew near, the newly matured animals grew restless.

The younger bulls, too, became more active, though for most it would be several summers yet before they reached a size which would allow them to compete for cows. Nonetheless, their periods of play became longer and were rougher than at other times. Some, particularly those approaching full maturity, became aggressive, openly challenging even the largest bulls for space on a resting rock, and in many cases being seen off by a swift bite to the neck or face. Every few seasons a new bull would fight fiercely with an old male in order to attain and confirm his breeding status, and a battle might continue for days until either he had won or was seen off. After being defeated, an older bull would depart until mating time was over, returning only after he had sulked in solitude for some weeks, his ire spent and the jealous rage of the younger animal who had replaced him gone, too, until the following summer.

For the cows, though, it was not a time to fight but to conserve. In the early days of summer those due to calve hunted hard, building their reserves so they would produce milk in plenty for their pups. As the Birthing Time of each approached they grew pensive and solitary, spending long periods on the outer edges of the colony and watching carefully each subtle change of tide and weather. Those that would breed for the first time often acted strangely, for as it had been since the days of The Seal Fathers, the consciousness of every beast was, at that time every year, channelled to a single purpose. An ancient, inexplicable chemistry was at work, and although the wider meaning of its purpose mattered not in the mind of any beast, its Message was clear to all. So it was, that as the first pup of that year was born, bull seals began to seek the company of cows.

*   *   *

That summer's Birthing was almost complete. Rondo had
watched as the new pups began to swim on their own around
Outer Bay as their mothers hunted, and sometimes had
tumbled gently with some of them as they played. Rondo
knew of changes in herself, but her natural reticence made
her a difficult target for the bulls who sought her company,
and soon found out about the one-eyed beast's reluctance to
be nosed or pushed around. First, she moved to the edge of
the colony to escape these attentions, but as they persisted
and grew more intense, Rondo swam south to her former
resting rock beside The Sound in order to find peace.

As the seal arrived she checked carefully for the presence
of other beasts and satisfied herself she was alone before
hauling out. But Rondo could not find freedom there, for all
around Northisle were youngsters who had been chased
from the main colony by the largest, most powerful bulls
until the rut was over, and all now looked for any opportunity to mate. Within an hour Rondo had been joined by a bull
of six summers, and then, a short time later by another, an
old and angry beast, newly defeated and driven out by a
stronger, much younger competitor.

The animal of six summers had hauled out a few seal's
lengths below Rondo and greeted her noisily. The older
beast had cruised round after he arrived, looking for any sign
of receptiveness from the one-eyed cow and trying to assess
the mood and strength of the bull already on the rock.
Wavelets slapped lazily on stone. The older beast approached and lay in the shallows, half submerged and looking side-
long at the other bull, exhaling loudly through his nose and
shaking his head, spraying water and pieces of weed about
him.

Rondo sharpened to the growing tension but feigned indif-
ference and made no attempt to move. The younger bull
held his ground, seemingly unaffected by the aggression of
the other save for a lifting of his head whenever the other
shook. The older bull was his cousin and he knew him well,
having already avoided a fight with him two days before. He
sized him, judging how far he might have travelled that day,
how tired he might be and for how many days he had fought

to retain his place at Northbay before his last defeat. How much of his aggression was bluff? Could the old bull back up his aggression with real power after the battles he had just fought, the scars of which still bled and stained his neck red.

The old bull moved up slowly, trying to conceal from the other the pain of his wounds. The younger tensed and bared his teeth, holding his head tilted back and over to one side, his eyes fixed. He remained silent as the old bull growled and ranted, slapping fore flippers in the shallows and winding his head from side to side. He was big, heavy and well fed. Power was in him: from jaw to tail was all the power of his Kind. But could he still use it? He had lost at Northbay. The young beast had yet to prove himself in battle, but he knew by The Ages that his time was to come.

For almost an hour the two beasts sparred, the younger facing down the other's noise, standing his ground and waiting. The tide had been dropping steadily to leave all three seals high and dry, and with tension rising, all felt vulnerable in some way. Yet none would make a move, not Rondo since she would be pursued by both bulls and might be injured, nor either bull, in case such action was construed as weakness, a sign of backing down which might give the other an advantage. Rondo was no longer as concerned with the presence of the younger beast as she had been when he arrived. He had not bothered her, had not even attempted to approach her yet; but the old beast, heavy, aggressive and noisy, worried her. Already, she had resolved to fight him should he make any move towards her.

The puttering of an unfamiliar engine drifted through The Sound to distract the seals, making all three look up and spy to the south-west. A small fishing boat, its single occupant standing in the stern, headed across The Sound towards Southisle. As it disappeared from view the old bull made his move. With speed that belied his size and age he was across the rock in seconds, and only when he began to haul noisily upward for the last two seal's lengths towards his rival did the other realise what was happening. He turned to face the older bull, spitting and growling, his closest fore limb raised, ready to flail and scratch his attacker. A land bound fight would end in victory for the older beast for his weight alone would crush the younger animal, and his teeth, once fastened, would inflict terrible wounds. The young bull knew he would be beaten there, but feinted and allowed the old beast to think he would stand fast, all the time seeking out the quickest passage to the water where his youth and speed would have a better chance to carry the fight. As the older seal began again to haul upwards, the other rolled to his left and twisted till he faced the sea, and then, with a single heave covered the steep slope, driving hard as he hit the water so he was submerged and out of sight before his rival had time to follow. Now, the old bull would have to be goaded into the water and the young beast could waste no time if he was to keep the initiative. He turned, sped to the surface and porpoised close to the rock, shaking his head violently with his teeth bared as he passed close to the other seal. Again he porpoised, and again, closer to the old bull with each pass until it was forced to respond by plunging angrily to the water's edge. Rondo was unsettled but still made no attempt to move. She heard the old bull snarl each time the younger animal broke surface and surged inwards with his teeth flashing, and the cow knew it could only be a matter of time before the older beast would be forced to take off in pursuit. She sat tight, waiting to be left alone.

The older bull entered the shallows. At his next pass the younger lashed out, nipping the other on the side of the neck and raising his elder's rage to fever pitch. He could take no more and lumbered fiercely after the youngster, snorting and shaking his scarred old head. He had power, but lacked the suppleness of his young rival who raced round him, nipping and butting, doing everything he could to tire the old beast, frustrating him, letting him know how inadequate his age had made him. The old animal would not give in and followed as the other dived deep to twist and weave among the kelp and wrack of the sea floor. He was waiting for the youngster to make a mistake but his ire was high and his temper got the better of him as the young seal baited him incessantly. Strength, experience and guile, all he had learned in years of fighting, to judge height and distance and anticipate another's moves, these things had, by now, been almost completely subjugated by the sheer desperation to win what might prove to be the last battle he would ever fight, but tired after so many days of warring he was bested in the chase repeatedly.

At last the two came face to face, the older all but exhausted, but his rival knowing that the other still had sufficient strength to kill if he was given the opportunity. Knowing he would have but a single chance to win, he waited, blowing bubbles and shaking his head, hanging in the clearness a dozen seal's lengths below the surface, taunting the tired, old animal, goading him, willing him to strike. The old bull called together all the power and strength of his eighteen summers. He had fathered his first pup more than a hundred moons before, but now his mastery faced a final test, exactly as had the first old bull he himself had beaten. In a last, desperate effort, almost blind with anger and with all the Rage of The Ages in him, he drove forward.

His speed surprised the youngster and left him little time to make a quick half-turn to avoid being winded as the old beast first slammed into his side then rolled and tried to find something on which his teeth could grip. The young bull felt the other's teeth brush his neck, but with the agility of youth, twisted, cartwheeling as he turned and found the big, blunt muzzle of the older seal. He clamped his jaws tight, and the other exhaled rapidly as the shock of the youngster's bite raced through him and he shuddered in pain. The old bull shook his head as hard as he could, but to no avail, for the youngster merely clenched harder to his muzzle. They drifted upwards, and now the younger began to twist and writhe, driving his teeth to the bone, so that by the time they reached the surface and were in full view of Rondo the battle was almost won.

There is a noiseless way of speaking among bird and beast which signifies the passage of the main events of life, and which all things understand. In such a way did the young bull know his task was done; and the older that his time as master was over. The young beast, with a last, telling shake, had let go, leaving his opponent to swim to the shallows at the far end of Rondo's rock. As he gained the surface he gasped for breath and blood ran from his grizzled old face as, still grunting defiantly he wiped his wounds with a fore flipper. He would need the rest of that summer to recover, but with luck, would live out his last few years in peace at Northbay. His victor stared hard at him from the waters edge, new self-knowledge calming him, his self assurance all but complete and knowing he had no more to do, that the old bull was finished and would not even have to be seen off. He would go from there as soon as pride allowed, leaving nothing but a splash of blood upon the rock.

The young bull settled, relaxed now in victory. Rondo remained in her place not wishing to move until the vanquished animal had finally left and still nervous after the vicious battle. But for the young beast's luck in holding on to the muzzle of the old warrior the fight may have lasted much longer and meant the death of either, or even both animals, but luck, though perversely for the older beast, had been with them both. Rondo had triggered the fight, but the prize of the young bull's victory went far beyond the right to mate with a single cow, for more than anything it was a major marker in the life of a bull seal, showing not only that he had survived infancy and youth, but had grown strong and was fit now to join the line of Seal Fathers which stretched back to before the time men learned to stand on two legs. His name was Phoca, and after the old bull had grumbled into the water and left to sulk for a few days in some secret place, he hauled high onto the rock beside Rondo One-Eye. He was tired now, but apart from a small bite on the side of his neck was unmarked by the fight. All he needed was a few hours of peace in which to rest.

Rondo slept most of the afternoon. When she woke Phoca was alert, hungry and already spying the water for signs. She felt somehow different, as though she had changed from the way she had been at Northbay, relaxed and with nothing to interfere with the quiet, uncomplicated life she led. Now, something urgent was nagging her. The cow began to preen. In the last few days she had begun her summer moult, and the new coat, in forcing itself through to replace the old, caused irritation. Tufts of hair had begun to loosen round her rear limbs which she rubbed hard on the rough rock, enjoying the relief it gave. She was hungry, and too warm after lying out in the strong sun. Phoca took to the sea, and Rondo needed no encouragement to follow.

They swam east from the reef then turned and headed north towards Creekharbour, moving gradually closer to the shore. Rondo overtook the young bull, and he followed closely as she dived and surfaced, searching for any chance of food. A small boat passed, a fisherman from Creekharbour on his way to haul lobster pots on the hard, rocky patches near The Sound. The seals dived again after he had gone and now the bull was closer, swerving and weaving so that he brushed continually against the cow.

Five hundred seal's lengths south of the entrance to Creekharbour was a sandy shoal which stretched out from the shore and had been marked by men with a large buoy so that their boats and ships would keep clear of the place. Rondo dived to nose the sand, feeling with her long whiskers for any movement of the Dabs and small Sole she knew to be hidden there. Phoca followed and hunted in the same way a few seal's lengths to her right, watching her, passing silent Messages and, from time to time, swerving playfully across her path as though trying to distract her. She disturbed a dab and made a grab for it, slashing sideways as it tried to flee, but Phoca drove forward, stealing the fish before she had a chance to close her teeth, and floated to the surface, tearing and leaving morsels of flesh and bone in his wake. Rondo waited. She lay still on the bottom and looked up through clear, shallow water, tensing herself. Phoca rolled on his back holding the dab between his front flippers, and as he began to crunch through the fish was rammed hard from below. He dropped it, already driving with his rear limbs and turning his head down in order to see his attacker. But Rondo was already on him, twisting to regain the fish then diving, steep and swift, heading for the deeps outside the shoal.

She surfaced only when she had gone two hundred seal's lengths and was well outside the buoy which marked the shallows. She ate quickly as Phoca swam to meet her.

Dropping the remains of the dab she dived below him and made for the rocky shoreline. The bull followed and the two seals played and hunted, knowing by The Ages that this was but a prelude to something more, something as ancient as time itself by which their Kind might thrive forever on the planet as they had done since the days of The Seal Fathers.

No wind disturbed the sea there. No breath swept even from the land to dim the shining mirror. They swam more slowly, more closely. They chased again, hiding, twisting and butting each other then rolling sinuously in the shallowest water where they were barely afloat; touching always, speaking gently, almost silently, in the tongue of their own Kind.

In the way of The Ages they joined. Then, as Phoca's seed ran in Rondo they separated and swam slowly north to a small resting rock at the outer edge of Creekharbour's winding channel, hauled out and slept. The Ages had been satisfied, and in almost a year, should all go well Rondo would bear her first pup.

Chapter 22

It grew cloudy and the wind rose to swirl around the rocks and cliffs as Rondo arrived at Northbay. She swam among the reefs for half an hour, unsettled by the sudden change in the weather and not wishing to haul out only to find she must move again later. Other seals, too, were becoming restless. There was a rising song in the wind which none liked and the cat's-paws grew and sped more and more quickly across the water, bending the tops of the old pines on the two outer islands. Rondo swam slowly into the channel to Inner Bay, still cautious, though some others had already moved in and lay high on the slabs along the west side of the gut, preening and settling to await the coming gale. Despite the wind's sound there was a stillness, almost a suspension of life as clouds piled high upon each other. The wind straightened and came out of the east. It strengthened and was turned by the headland on the edge of Outer Bay to blow directly into the narrow gut; funnelled now, concentrated; ruffling the coats of seals that were huddled under the overhangs, all knowing by The Ages that with the wind from this direction there could be no effective escape from the blast. Clouds began to tumble, emptying rain into the wind, and the eiders bobbed together in the water under the lee of the cliffs opposite the seals, their necks drawn down and their beaks laid on puffed out breast feathers as they rode the squalls.

Despite the coming gale Rondo was relaxed in herself. She knew she was changed and that her mating with Phoca was to alter her life. It would be some time before she felt the pup growing inside her, for in the way The Ages had provided for her Kind, the mixing of her own and Phoca's seed would not begin to develop further for four moons or more, and it would be snowmelt before she felt any real presence of the new life. So it had been for Rondo's Kind since the days of The Seal Fathers, and now, under the gale, beneath the driving rain and spray she found the best lee she could and settled back to sleep.

Life at Northbay continued peacefully for the rest of that summer. The big gale which had arrived as Rondo returned after mating signalled a long period of windy, unsettled weather, and it was late September before the sun shone steadily again, day after day. The family who had sold the dwelling returned briefly to remove what belonged to them, but due to the bad weather, few yachts visited the place, leaving the seals almost undisturbed. So it remained right into autumn and until the time snow first appeared on mainland mountains. Then, in the short days of early winter when Rondo's Kind had begun to spread out again in search of food, two men came to the house above Inner Bay.

The lights remained on until two or three hours after dark each evening. Bricks, timber and other goods were brought down the narrow road by truck and stored in the shed behind the house and outside under black, plastic sheets which shone brightly and flickered when the sun was on them. There was not much noise, and though the seals were curious they were not frightened by what was going on. Some swam into Inner Bay as dusk approached and lay in the shallows close to the beach, watching as the men carried things to and fro, long into the evening. There were hammering and sawing noises, but the beasts became used to them and soon ignored all the activity, knowing the men would not come near them and that they posed no threat. For some weeks on either side of the solstice the men's visits became patchy until, in early February when frosts were in the ground they returned no more. Their absence was all but unnoticed by the seals of Northbay. The bricks still stood in a stack outside the house, and when the wind blew, the plastic sheeting flapped noisily with cracking sounds.

Rondo moved occasionally to her old resting rock beside

The Sound, for food was scarce without the great summer shoals and each of her Kind had favoured places for use at such times. For the one-eyed cow the area around The Sound provided all she needed to sustain herself, and when the sea was too rough to allow her to remain there she took to hauling out in a new place, a slab among some tumbled boulders only a hundred seal's lengths south of the ferry pier outside Creekharbour. She was protected there from wind and sea and, more importantly, was hidden from the bustle on the pier when, three days a week, the boat arrived from Southisle and the mainland. As the days lengthened she explored further, sometimes returning late in the night after searching the coastline of Southisle or the shallow banks which lay off its south side. Rondo became expert at hunting in darkness, for fish move more readily in shallow water during the hours when light from above is cut almost to nothing, feeling safer, perhaps, from hunters such as seals or fish larger than themselves. Even with her single eye she became able to pick out the slightest movement, remembering all the knowledge she had gained of fish and where their lodges could be found, and by using the patience and stealth she had learned among the mackerel shoals.

She grew aware of the pup growing inside her and by Snowmelt The Ages had spoken, telling her to feed and fatten. She went about it in a careful, controlled way. When hunting was easy and there was plenty to be had she continued longer, catching all she could so long as she still gained over the effort she used. If the weather was bad or when strong, turbulent tides made it difficult to reach the most productive hunting grounds she would remain at rest, either in Northbay or on her resting rocks by Creekharbour or at The Sound.

Rondo One-Eye flourished. Of her mate Phoca there was little sign and he appeared now at Northbay only occasionally. In summer, after the pups were born and breeding cows came again to the time when they would mate, the young bull would return to re-establish his role as a bull in full maturity. When Rondo's pup was six weeks old, should all be well, she would mate again with Phoca, and as a tribute to The Ages and her recovery from all the trials of her youth, should go on breeding for perhaps another fifteen summers until she grew old and tired. Here at Northbay and in the waters around the two islands and The Sound she had found the finest of places to live her life; a place where seals and every other bird and beast were still able to live according to the Ways and Messages of The Ages: where there was no greed among those things and each took only as The Ages had provided. There were neither too many of any Kind, – not even of men, nor too few. The balance among all things was correct. The Ages were heeded.

*   *   *

Late in April men returned to Northbay and began to work around the house. To begin with the seals were not disturbed, but after a week or so a large digger arrived and roared continuously for long periods as it tore into the thin soil of the sloping fields above Inner Bay, digging holes and trenches. Most of the seals did not move far away, resting instead on outer rocks and skerries. At length they grew used to the noise and moved back to their places on favourite islets, looking up curiously at the work done by the digger, which from a seal's viewpoint, were a strange series of straight lines and squares, covering the fields almost to the very edge of the short cliff on the far side of the channel.

The fields, which by then should have been carpeted with grasses and spring blooms, had become bare and brown, stripped of all that had grown there for generations. That small piece of ground, the only green at the Isle's north end, once so full of life with insects, voles and other creatures, every one, another's food, had now been ravaged. Roe deer and hares would come no more at dusk to feed throughout the nights of spring and summer on sweet, new grass. Kestrel and buzzard would be seen no longer in the blue above, and all things, every bird and beast and blade that once had used that small, mean field as larder, nursery or dwelling, would know a time of dearth.

One afternoon a large lorry roared over the brow of the

hill, its engine straining under the weight it carried. It was followed by a crane, and the seals watched in fear as the long, yellow jib was run out to stand high above the house, pointing to the clouds. The lorry was unloaded and the materials it had carried spread around the buildings. It left, but returned twice over the next week, each time bringing a fresh load of bricks, timber and bags of cement. More men appeared, then more again, until at the beginning of May there were five caravans parked by the old house, each occupied by three or four men.

Some came to sit by the rocks or on the beach at midday or late in the evening after they had finished work. More equipment had been brought in, and now, early each morning the silence was broken by the sounds of diggers and cement mixers which roared throughout the day. The seals became more and more disturbed, not only by the noise but by some of the men who walked the shoreline in the evenings to fish, throwing their lines far out among the skerries and rocks and throwing stones at the seals to make them clear off in case their gear might be fouled by the beasts.

Rondo and the others were confused and sometimes frightened. The whole face of the place in which they and their ancestors had always lived was being changed. New houses were being built and the road had been widened. Lorries arrived every few days and the only time the seals were able to find peace in their own place was during the shortening, dark hours. Soon it would be pupping time, and it was vital that the cows and pups were not be not disturbed. Then, towards the end of May when mackerel shoals should be approaching the coast, the boats arrived.

There were two. One a sturdy workboat, deep and wide and with a small crane mounted near the stern, and the other a fast inflatable, driven by a powerful, noisy outboard. The big yellow crane was driven on to the beach and the jib swung out over the bay. The workboat had a machine on board which sucked up all the mud and sand, throwing it far out to one side. They dredged a channel to the new pier for which the crane now began to drive the piling. Steel pipes were put and held in place by the boats as the big crane dropped a heavy weight onto them, driving them deep into the bottom. When they were firm enough, the real damage began, for then cement was poured into the pipes and leaked into the bay killing everything it came into contact with by denying oxygen to all the creatures of the mud and sand.

When the short, stubby pier was complete, timber decked pontoons were attached to it, and on the day the boats began to run out the long chains and anchors to hold those in position, a spring gale blew in from the north east without warning. It was from the worst direction for the seals. The wind was cutting and brought with it heavy showers of driving, cold rain and then hail. Normally the beasts would have left their rocks and headed inwards, at least as far as the narrow gut, and many, right into Inner Bay. But that option was denied them, for the forest of buildings which had grown round the old dwelling and its cattle shed and all the noise of so many people now ensured that Inner Bay could no longer be used by the seals as they had used it since so long before the time of man.

As the gale blew in the seals stayed on the outer skerries, cold and miserable, and by the time it had passed most had taken to the water where they were warmer. But what if the gale had come in winter and been stronger and more sustained. What if it had lasted two, three days or more, so that the seals would have needed desperately to use the shelter only afforded by Northbay?

Yet again the hand of man had touched the Northlands. The seals had no part in it. The eider and the otter, the cormorant, the roe deer which had grazed for thousands of years in the small field now in ruins; the geese of winter, every small bird, every insect. None had taken more than they had needed since before the time of man. Now all were to be displaced by a few, wealthy people from the south who required a view. But there would be no lights shining out over Northbay on winter nights, no voices on those cold crisp days, for despite the new houses, despite the pier and its pontoons and the new poles which now marked the channel, all these things were for the use of men only during

the summer. Then there would be noise. Then there would
be voices, shouting, boats, engines; but there would be no
roe deer or eider duck, and there would be no seals either,
resting on the rocks and skerries of The Seal Fathers.

*   *   *

Towards the end of May Rondo had become more and
more aware of the pup growing inside her. It moved occasionally and she watched the tides and weather carefully,
avoiding any action which required great effort and making
sure her hunting trips were close to Northbay so she did not
use up more energy than she could replace. Most of the work
had been finished above Inner Bay and the noise had
decreased, but still, there were too many people there for
safety, so many beasts and birds simply wandered away to
try and find a new, more peaceful home. They would have
to travel far.

Then, when summer days were already almost as long as
they could be and the sun was high and hot from early
morning, a great gathering of people took place among the
new houses of Northbay. The time of the official opening of
the development had come. Some had travelled by ferry to
the island and then over the hill by car, shouting loudly as
soon as they arrived. Others came by boat, and for two days
there were over twenty yachts moored in Inner Bay. After
they had all passed, waving and whistling at the seals, hardly
a beast was left.

Boats came and went through the channel taking parties
of prospective buyers out to sea to show them how wonderful the place was and how close they were to the finest
scenery and the best sailing in all Europe. Men had been
working almost all day on the west headland, and only
Rondo and a few others had remained, those with more
experience of men and who could judge their moods more
accurately than the rest. On what was to be the final day of
celebration, late in evening the gathering increased. Rondo
had found a spot on an outer skerry close to one of the two,
large islets which marked the channel entrance. At dusk, the

noise from inside the bay became subdued and strangely quiet. There were not so many voices and no one walked the shore or meandered through the channel in boats as had been happening for the past few days.

It was just before midnight when the first lights lit the sky. A dozen stars burst in green and red above Northbay and fell silently towards the west. Then, the storm of light and noise began. Starbursts, trails of brilliant coloured light, a thousand meteors brightened the night sky above the seals of Northbay. It was as if all the lightning of a thousand years had come on them at once. Explosions filled the air and mixed with the sounds of excited, shouting, human voices. On the west headland only fifty seal's lengths from where Rondo and the others lay, the second phase of the display was about to begin and they watched in growing fright as the shadows of men moved round by the light of torches as they made ready.

The explosions began anew and as the light increased and glowed constantly, a single thought came to Rondo's mind. It was of the pool in which she had been imprisoned; the noise, the lights she hated so much and which had almost driven her to madness. She plunged from her rock as she saw the first rocket shoot from the headland and race upwards, a trail of sparks in its wake. She hit the water, already diving to the bottom then following its line and swimming northwards as fast as she could. She cleared the channel but did not stop, still driving with her rear limbs, intent only on gaining as much distance as she could from the rock before rising to breathe. The bottom dropped away steeply but she held her line, maintaining a constant depth five or six seal's lengths below the surface, driving hard to clear the coast and reach the safety she knew was to be found to the north. At length, she was forced to rise. Filling her lungs she turned to look back towards Northbay and saw again the maelstrom it had become. Around her were other beasts, for all had fled in terror and now looked back towards their home; the home of all the generations that had lived, had bred, had enjoyed. All the generations since the days of The Seal Fathers that had known the kindness and shelter of Northbay. But all that was now as nothing. Lit up like a small town, Northbay was officially open, and the colony of Rondo One-Eye's Kind was closed forever.

Chapter 23: The Voyage

The first part of the voyage, from a shipyard in Spain to the oil terminal on an island beyond the highest latitudes of the Northlands, had gone reasonably well. The captain had had misgivings about some of the new crew his owners had sent to the ship, for two of the officers were not only very young and inexperienced, but showed poor command of English which is the common language of the sea. From what the captain could tell, both the officers appeared keen and efficient, but already they had found trouble communicating with others on board. There had, too, been some confusion over orders he had given when about to leave the oil terminal for the return voyage to Europe with their full cargo of crude oil, and although nothing serious had happened as a result, it continued to worry him that he could be so easily misunderstood.

The route to their next port, in Northern Europe, looked deceptively simple. They would pass through the firth that separated the Northlands from where they had loaded their cargo and follow the western seaboard of Scotland inside the long line of islands called the Hebrides, before passing between the Green Isle and the Southlands where Rondo had been imprisoned. Left to himself, the captain would have chosen a different way from the one he was to take, bringing his ship outside the Isles of The Hebrides and the Green Isle and keeping at least twenty miles from the coast in order to leave plenty of sea room in case of fog or other weather problems, or, what every shipmaster fears most, an engine breakdown close to the shore. But the vessel's owners insisted on the shortest possible route always being taken, regardless of conditions or hazards, so though the captain was only too well aware that wherever there was a ship with a cargo such as his there was bound to be danger, and that the closer to land they were the more that danger increased, he had no choice but to follow his owners' orders and take the shorter route. Until quite recently, other than in wartime large ships such as his had seldom been seen near such a dangerous coast until it was time for them to approach their port of call, but nowadays that had changed, and in using the route between the oil terminal and some European ports, shipowners saved a full twelve hours by making sure their ships were routed inside the Hebrides rather than on the safer, outside passage. The days when a ship's master was in sole charge of the conduct of a voyage had long since passed, money ruled now and his instructions from his employers were clear; if there was a way of saving even a few hours, he had to take it. Only in such ways, they said, could they remain competitive and stay in business.

He knew then that he must remain especially alert, particularly with new, unproven crew on board, and he made it doubly clear to all the officers concerned with the navigation of the vessel that he required an accurate plot of the ship's passage to be kept at all times as well as a careful, visual lookout for anything that could prove to be a risk. They must not, he told them, place too much reliance on radar or any of the rest of the vast array of electronic aids commonplace on modern ships. Everything must be double checked, and if anyone was in any doubt they were to call him immediately. It was of some comfort to him that these were the long days of summer when there was daylight in these latitudes from four in the morning until after ten at night, but his doubts lingered about the two, new men, and he hoped they had understood fully the importance of his instructions.

The ship passed its first obstacle, the narrow channel of the firth which led out to the western seaboard, without incident. She came abreast of the stark, rocky point called by men, Cape Wrath, then ran on to the west a full fifteen miles before turning south into The Sea of The Hebrides. This meant that after she turned she would be in the centre of the channel between islands and mainland, giving her the maximum amount of room should she have to manoeuvre to avoid another vessel, or for any other reason.

The captain checked the chart once again. The run on this leg was a distance of about seventy miles from the turning point. Towards the lower end of the track, about sixty miles from where the ship now was, lay a scattered, dangerous group of reefs and islets. There was no lighthouse there, only a few buoys with flashing lights to mark them, and at the point of the ship's closest approach, for about half an hour the navigable channel would be less than less than two miles wide between the rocks and the mainland. Special care would be necessary when approaching and passing through that area, which would begin about four hours after their turn to the south, so he left a note in the log book instructing that he should be called when they were five miles away, and that their speed was to be reduced by one third at the same time. He looked at the bridge clock and saw that it was just before ten. They would be down there by two in the morning and since he had been working continuously for almost sixteen hours already that day he decided to steal a few hours rest. Before going down to his cabin he went out onto the open bridge wing to look around one last time, and though he had seen many wonderful things during a long career at sea, he still marvelled at the clear dusk and the darkening lines of ridges and summits of the great Northland mountains that showed clearly on the mainland side. The visibility, he reckoned, was over thirty miles. The watch keeping officer on the bridge would change at midnight when one of the new men would take over, but still, he thought, there should be no problems on such a fine, clear night.

Dusk continued to gather as the ship steamed on. There was no breeze, the sea like glass and cut only by the vessel's wake, a wide, tall V which caught the last of light as it rolled over on itself and tumbled into pure, white foam. Lights from both shores could be seen clearly, singly from scattered farms and cottages, and sometimes as moving, twisting beams, as cars travelled along hilly, coastal roads. And from the shore, too, the ship could be seen, a large, black shadow standing tall above the sea , her true length only discernible to a practised eye which could judge the distances between her glowing navigation lights.

And the creatures below the waves knew of her presence, though not by sight, for the heavy thrum of her engines and the steady beat of her massive propeller carried in waves of sound and vibration for many miles under the surface, so all knew of the monster that passed above and remained wary until her sound began to fade.

On the bridge the captain's orders were followed to the letter. The ship's position was plotted on the chart every fifteen minutes so every deviation from her intended course could be corrected. As midnight approached, she was exactly where she was supposed to be.

★   ★   ★

Gerda, in the Way of her Kind, had travelled far. She had come to these islets last autumn after a journey that had taken her far from the waters of Loch Shiel where, as a yearling, she had befriended the one-eyed pup. Now she was among her own Kind, the grey beasts of the Atlantic who's Way was to travel most of the year following the harvests of the great deeps until a declining sun and the gales and cold north winds of autumn called them in their hundreds to the same steep beaches that were the Birthing Rocks of their generations, and where their Seal Fathers had roared their Messages long before man touched the Northlands.

Like Rondo she had grown well. She was no longer so slim and elegant as when a yearling, having filled out as she fed well and built the blubber layer she must maintain through adulthood. The journey she had made after leaving Loch Shiel had taken her far into the Northland seas where she had hunted among her own Kind, learning more with each new moon. Far to the west, she had hauled that autumn onto a long, steep gravel beach where the bulls roared and the cows arrived, first to give birth and then to breed again. Gerda, not yet fully mature, had not mated that autumn, but only watched as the year's new pups grew and moulted their downy, white coats before taking to the water and beginning the long voyage to survival.

After the birthing and mating time had come the yearly moult of the adults, and Gerda had sloughed her now bedraggled coat and grown in the new. She tarried until nearly all the other beasts had left, then followed as the last of them dispersed to seek the shoals of whiting and herring. She continued to learn from others of her Kind, and soon enough, began also to know the ways and sounds of other creatures of the deeps. She had met leviathans, sperm and humpback whales, and sought shelter as at first, fear gripped her as their songs echoed in the ocean around her. Then, as she came to realise the beasts were not a danger to her she grew complacent, nearly losing her life to a female sperm whale after she had approached its yearling calf and the great beast drove at her, ready to crush her in an instant and leave her broken body to the crabs and fishes. But in such ways she came to learn to leave alone what was clearly powerful or dangerous, and after a year or so of travelling, had grown as wise as any of her Kind.

Spring had found her west of the Hebrides, well fed and confident. As a series of gales had driven towards the line of islands she had swum east with the weather and passed through a narrow sound into the waters of what men call, The Minch. Here there was food for her, and she wandered the full length and breadth of those waters, coming to know the tides, the reefs and the safest places to haul out in different winds and swells.

She had just hauled out after spending an hour combing the long reef which ran out to the west, for rock cod. By now, though, the moon had risen too high, and the fish had returned to their lodges to hide. Her resting rock gave a clear view to the north, and as she began to doze she sensed a sound she already knew well. It was a ship, and soon, from the beat of engine and propeller vibrating through the rock on which she lay she would know also how close it was and the direction in which it was travelling. She looked out but saw only the moon. The noise and vibration of ships passing here were commonplace, so she shuffled round to find the most comfortable spot, then drifted into sleep.

*   *   *

The watch on the bridge changed at midnight and one of the new officers took over. The note the captain had left was pointed out to him, the log book initialled, and the ship's position carefully plotted then double checked. On the chart the course line was quite clear, straight down the middle of the channel between the island group and the mainland shore, the vessel's nearest approach to each being just under a mile.

All was quiet, and under the moon the mainland skyline was still clearly visible to the left. The new officer had been told the tide had turned at ten o-clock and that the stream would be running strongly in a southerly direction until three when it would begin to slacken. The current would give the ship some extra speed, but would also mean that should anything untoward happen, the distance required to bring her to a stop, even using the engines, would be increased to over three miles.

At fifteen minutes after midnight, as the captain had instructed, the ship's position was plotted on the chart, this time, using both radar and satellite navigation systems. The radar had been set to sound an alarm should the ship stray more than a quarter of a mile off her intended track, but the young officer, though unfamiliar both with these waters and the ship, reset the alarm to half a mile, thinking the previous setting was over cautious. The tide could easily push them such a small distance off course over fifteen minutes, and he didn't want alarms sounding all the time. He thought, too, that plotting a position every fifteen minutes was over the top. In his opinion, with so much modern equipment on the bridge, half an hour was ample time between plots. He checked the radar again. According to the rangefinder the nearest of the islands was twenty seven miles distant. Looking good, he thought, straight down the middle. He went out to the bridge wing and spoke to the lookout posted there: there were no other vessels in sight, everything was fine.

When twelve thirty came around the officer was making himself a cup of coffee in the chartroom to the rear of the bridge. He had missed the exact time for his plot so marked the chart where he thought the ship had been on the half hour. The duty engineer arrived a few minutes later for a chat and to ask if he could borrow the lookout to help him refit a valve. He had no one else on watch in the engine room to help him and he said it would only take ten minutes. By the time they had finished talking it was after one. The ship had travelled nearly nine miles since the last plot, but again, the officer marked her position as where he thought she should have been, and took only a cursory glance at the radar to check his guesswork. He knew they had plenty of room.

The captain had intended merely to doze on his bunk, but the long hours he had worked over the previous week had caught up with him. He had also had the stress of tricky navigation getting into the oil terminal for their cargo, and this, coupled with his worries about some of his new crew members and the pressure of the mountain of paperwork, all to be accurately and quickly completed after loading the ship, had ensured that exhaustion was inevitable.

When he woke suddenly he realised his telephone hadn't rung. He looked at his watch and saw that it was one-thirty. A quick calculation told him they must be close to five miles from the narrowest part of the channel, but seeing nothing from the window of his cabin but a calm sea, he went for a quick wash before going up to the bridge.

*   *   *

Gerda looked up, wakened by seabirds chattering on the rocks around her. She felt strong vibration through the rock and heard clearly the steady beat of a ship's engine. There were lights now, too, and birds, gulls and fulmar petrels were taking off and flying towards them. But they seemed to be to the west of where they were usually seen from that rock: and they were closer than she had seen them before. Other seals nearby were becoming uneasy, shuffling round so they pointed towards the sea and stretching their necks and heads towards the noise, their senses sharpening, all of them ready for a quick escape.

Just as the captain finished drying his face he heard the engine die. Lights dimmed or went out as the emergency battery system took over. Alarm klaxons were sounding as he ran out of his cabin and began to take the stairway to the bridge three steps at a time, and he was aware that he hadn't heard the emergency generator cut in, as it should have done immediately the power failed. Why the hell wasn't it working? It had been overhauled only two weeks ago in the ship repair yard!

He went straight to the chart and checked the last plot, made less than five minutes before. It showed them seven miles clear of the nearest rock and right in the middle of the channel. From this position there should be enough way on the vessel to steer her away from the passage and safely out to seaward to a point where they could anchor and get the engines sorted out in safety.

Going through into the bridge he found the officer of the watch, ashen faced and holding the telephone. He had been trying to call him. "Get a position on to the chart, now" he barked. He looked into the radar but both sets were down. The emergency batteries supplied minimal power, enough only for dim lighting and the radio and ship's telephone systems: the radars couldn't be used until the emergency generator was running. He grabbed the telephone and tried calling the engine room, but no one answered, – they were all too busy trying to get the generator started. When he went on to the bridge wing the lookout was nowhere to be seen so he couldn't send him down to find out what was happening.

"Where's the bloody lookout" he yelled. Then, as he turned to enter the bridge again he stopped dead in his tracks and stared towards the bow. Ahead of them, less than a mile away, the shape of an island was clearly outlined against the sky.

The seals had heard the engine die and felt the vibration fade as the propeller slowly stopped turning. But though this should have settled them, they could still hear the heavy hiss of the ship's wake, and those in the water had already begun to feel the surge of the bow wave and the massive volume of water a ship of that size pushed ahead and to each side of her. In the engine room, panic had all but broken out. They had first tried desperately to restore power, but the job of refitting the valve the duty engineer had taken the lookout to help him with had gone disastrously wrong, and lubricating oil had poured into the engine compartments, splashing over hot metal and electrical switchboards, causing the ship's fire safety systems to cut the engine. Until the leak could be stopped and the switchboards cleaned there was too much risk of fire and explosion to restart the engine. The engineers could only curse. The job should never have been started in such close proximity to land, they said, but all knew that taking such risks was part and parcel now of life at sea, with everyone under continuous pressure to cut costs and get things done quickly.

The whole ship's company was now involved in efforts to save the vessel. On the bridge the young officer of the watch was muttering incoherently, and only the captain and chief officer had remained cool, the latter already on his way forward, racing across the two hundred metres of deck to the bow to release both anchors in a desperate effort to slow down or stop her before she struck. The master stared ahead of him, his eyes transfixed on the island, hoping against hope that the anchors would hold. The wheel had been turned hard to port as soon as he had realised how close they were, in a last, desperate attempt to try to bring her clear of the first island, but beyond that were more reefs and rocks. She had already slowed considerably, he knew, but was still travelling at a good six knots and with the tide pushing her down onto the islands. Still, he thought, there must be a chance.

There was a wild, uncontrolled rattle as both anchors went to the bottom. The captain knew that the water was already shoaling rapidly as they closed with the islands. The ship's draft was over twenty metres. He doubted if they had more than fifteen metres below the keel by now and within a few more minutes it would be much less. The chief officer put the brakes on both anchors when a hundred metres of chain was out on each, hoping that, helped by the weight of the long chains, they would dig in and bring her to a stop. But only a bottom of heavy sand or mud would allow that, and what was below them now was slimy, weed covered rock, on which the anchors slid and bounced as they were pulled along by the vast power and momentum of the fully loaded ship. Gerda, now in the water with all the other seals, heard the clamour of chain and anchors being dragged across the rocky sea bed, and watched as the great towering beast ploughed slowly towards their reef.

The ship struck while still travelling at three knots, tearing huge holes in the thick steel of her hull before lurching heavily and grinding to a halt less than a hundred metres from Gerda's resting rock. Almost immediately the gaseous smell of crude oil began to pervade every part of the stricken ship. The captain held an emergency briefing on the bridge. There was to be an immediate damage assessment. Everything had to be done to ensure they minimized any worsening of the situation. A Mayday signal was sent out and the coastguard contacted, but only after the captain had telephoned his owners by satellite link. He told them he thought it unlikely that the ship could be towed off unless some of his cargo was first removed on to other vessels so they wouldn't be lying so deep in the water. They told him he was on his own for the moment: everything now would be up to the emergency services and the ship's insurers.

As the enormity of the nightmare he was living through struck, his mind went blank. There was so much to do as the emergency response got under way, but he was in deep shock and could concentrate on none of it. Walking aimlessly through the bridge he saw, out on the wing, the young navigating officer who had done this to him. He had a chart in his hands which he was tearing up and throwing over the side. He went towards him and looked straight into his eyes. They were lit with fear. Before he could stop himself he struck him full in the face with every ounce of power his frame could muster. Blood spurted from the man's nose as he crumpled soundlessly against the steel bulwark rail. The captain leaned over him and tried to drag him to his feet, as though about to send him, too, into the sea along with the evidence he had just destroyed and the oil which was spreading mercilessly now, carried by the tide and already beginning to envelope the rocks and islands they had foundered among.

He stopped suddenly and looked around. Dawn was breaking over the Northlands and its high, mainland mountains. He realised it was the most beautiful sight he had ever seen. The smell of oil returned to his nostrils and he looked over the side to see a bird, a fulmar petrel, floundering in the black, sticky mass, its wings half outstretched and flapping strongly but ineffectually as it tried in vain to take flight and escape, its neck stretched forward and its beak grotesquely agape as it struggled to draw breath through the filth that had already lined its throat and nostrils. When he raised his head again he was sobbing violently, his shoulders heaving and his knuckles, chalk white as he gripped hard on the rail, almost as though its steel might provide the strength he now needed. He, solely, was to blame for this. He alone would carry the blame which would cling as the oil was clinging to that bird, to his family, his children and their children, for as long as any of them lived.

He knew that his ship's owners, who had sent him here, by this route, would accept no responsibility for any of what had happened. They would say that the conduct of any voyage was the sole responsibility of the master and the law would agree. There was no record of any of their instructions, their cost cutting and time saving. Such things were never done on paper or in front of witnesses, for the owners knew the risk in that and took care to follow the words of their expensive lawyers. He looked back at the fulmar and saw himself as no different from the bird, now drowning in the stinking, black slime.

He looked round as he heard the officer he had knocked over struggling to his feet. He lashed out at him with a foot and the man screamed and half crawled back towards the safety of bridge. The rail was close by. The captain climbed onto it, his breathing deep and heavily laboured. He closed his eyes and leaned forward slightly. As a picture of his wife and children flashed through his mind, he jumped into the sea.

In the full dawning of a calm, almost idyllic day, the peace was shattered as television and newspaper reporters began to arrive in quickly and expensively hired boats, planes and helicopters. Most of the ship's crew were lifted to safety by helicopter, and salvage experts were lowered to decide on a course of action. As the full extent of the devastation the grounding would cause became evident to the world at large, fingers began to be pointed in any convenient direction. The government announced that an enquiry was to be set up immediately under the chairmanship of a distinguished judge, but to seafarers everywhere, to environmental groups and those few members of the wider public who had any real notion of how horrific the consequences of the event could prove to be, experience had already taught them that nothing would change if it were to cost money. Far away from the Northlands in the great cities of Europe, the vessels insurers, their accountants and lawyers, were already busy preparing to minimise the claims. The owners had refused to comment publicly until, they said, they had a full report from the vessels master.

When it emerged that the captain had jumped into the sea and was missing and presumed drowned, the shipowners, insurers and others who's responsibility it was to ensure that ships and their voyages were conducted in safety, began to breathe more easily, for now they had someone to blame who could not answer back. The young officer whose laziness and incompetence had been responsible for what had come about, and who had then watched the captain jump but done nothing to prevent him, was quickly put on a plane by his employers and removed to his own, distant country. The other crew members were similarly dispersed and ordered to say nothing. Since they knew all too well the consequences for their future careers, prospects and perhaps even their personal safety should anyone speak out, they all did exactly as they were told.

From the foundered ship, oil haemorrhaged into The Sea of The Hebrides. She was fast on an uneven, jagged reef for over fifty metres of her two hundred and fifty metre length, and though only three of her tanks had been ruptured, the whole hull might easily twist, breaching internal bulkheads or pipework and allowing oil to flow freely from any number of her forty or so cargo tanks into the ruptured sections. Soundings of the water depth all round her were made by the ancient method of using a marked line with a weight at its end, and the salvage experts who's aim was to avoid the total loss of the vessel and her cargo, realised quickly that she couldn't be floated and towed off without further damage unless some of her cargo was first transferred to another vessel, a procedure that was not only very hazardous but expensive. The easiest, quickest and cheapest way to lighten her to the point where she could be towed off was to allow as much oil as possible to flow into the sea by directing it into the torn tanks from those still intact. She would then rise bodily, and with the assistance of a powerful tug could be dragged clear on the next high tide. Money and speed were the prime considerations: the vast quantity of oil that would strangle and pollute for generations the pure waters of the Northlands, its creatures and people, was never part of the equation. Of course, discussion of the plan was held in utmost secrecy, and the story given to the world's press, very different from the real events that would take place, unseen by eyes or cameras.

Gerda and the seals swam nervously outside the range of the thick slick of oil. Its stench filled their nostrils, guaranteeing, ironically, that most would flee and escape its worst effects. The Ages could tell them nothing of this, but to Gerda as much as to many other beasts, the way was rapidly becoming clear, and she knew she would have to move from here right now. She had already swum beneath the oil, seen how the light was cut out by its spread and had sensed danger in what she could not understand. She had gone towards her resting rock, but already the black slime was clinging to its margins and she saw there seabirds, struggling helplessly to escape. The tide had begun to rise again. This time it would carry the slick north, then again south when it ebbed once more, further and further, surrounding and clinging to every resting rock, smothering every kelp and mussel bed, all on its way to the mainland shore to blacken the pure white sand of its beaches and spread when the wind rose, as it surely would, to pollute even the highest cliffs of the coast as it was blown from the sea as foam. Nothing here would escape its deathly grip, and The Sea of The Hebrides would die under it, all the work of The Ages undone, and yet one more pure place of Planet Earth destroyed by The Hand of Man.

Gerda made off to the south, swimming steadily and ignoring all that she had left behind, her mind fixed only on her own safety and in surviving as The Ages required. By daybreak she had reached a headland she recognised, and as she approached the high cliffs under which she knew she would find the steep gravel beach so favoured by her Kind, she stopped and held her head high out of the water, sniffing the air and looking round as though sensing something. Within a mile of her, Rondo One-Eye made steadily towards the coast.

Epilogue

Throughout that night Rondo had swum steadily to the north. The weather was calm and she dozed in the water from time to time with only her nose showing above the surface as she took her rest. As day broke she was well away from Northisle which now could no longer be seen even as a blur on the horizon. Far from the landward coast and any of the islands which stood to its west, Rondo would have to make a landfall soon for the water was too deep there for her to hunt effectively without knowing the ground and she must eat well and regularly if her strength and reserves were to remain in good heart. For the moment her pup was safe, but she had only a few weeks in which to settle, to find a place that was safe from men and the things she had seen in the last weeks, and one where she would also find the feeding she must have to provide milk for her pup.

For three days her path was northward and she managed to find shallow banks on which to hunt and feed. On the fourth morning the sun rose in a cloudless sky and all around was clear and sharp. From the crests of swells she was able to see the mainland coast, and to her north, the high tops of a large island. But there was something else which came to her. It was something not of vision nor of smell nor sound; but something, perhaps, born out of all the Messages of The Ages, a sense that came out of the mind, the memory of all her Kind since the days of The Seal Fathers.

As she approached the island to her north the sense grew stronger. On her eastern side a large gap had begun to open in the mainland coast between two ranges of high, brown hills. She had never swum these waters, never seen the island

that stood in her path, but still, there was something familiar, something about the sea's salinity and its taste which was
changing and becoming more familiar, minute by minute.
Without thinking further she turned and swam towards the
gap.

Something was driving her now, a force completely in
tune with her will to bear her pup, to feed and rest as her
body demanded. She needed no encouragement, no explanation of the urge to move as men might do. She accepted
simply that she must follow the lines of hills to wherever it
would lead. By nightfall she had gained the southern coast of
the gap and then, as she took her bearings and tried to make
some sense of where she was, a land breeze grew from the
north east. It carried scents that she had known in a time she
could barely remember, and as she lay on the surface tasting
wind and water, searching the horizon and the sea below for
some stronger sign, she felt the tide turn to the ebb and knew
in its flow the feel of Big Firth and the unmistakable smell of
The Narrows.

Dusk crept over the coast. The pup moved in Rondo One-
Eye as she cleared the tall cliffs of The Narrows, taking in all
she saw, searching, scouring hill and shore for every
memory, each familiar sight or smell. She closed with Black
Rocks, skirting them slowly as she approached, checking for
men and bird or beast before she dared to haul, for the past
few weeks had made her more careful than she had ever
been. From the signs within her and from the sea and sky,
she knew that it would not be long before the pup would
come. The tide was not yet big enough, nor had the moon
reached its zenith and begun to fall away again as it should
by Birthing Time. There could be as much as a quarter
moon yet to go and Rondo knew she must continue to feed
hard.

Before men were awake Rondo was close to Birthing
Rock. She had known as soon as she awoke that she must
make first for Bay of Otters then move north-east along the
line of North Shore to find the mud banks and their scores
of fat angler fish. Birthing Rock was on her path and she
checked for other seals around the islet of her birth. She

swam across Loch Shiel, its sights and sounds flooding her
with memories and the tallness of Dun Mountain's peaks
glowing pink in the early sun. As she approached the far side
of the loch she stopped. Something was different, changed.

A dozen cages had been moored in Bay of Otters. Behind
them, running up from the shore was a slipway and some
sheds. Piles of rubbish lay around and there was a rotten
smell which drifted out to the seal as she moved slowly inwards to investigate. She sensed the presence of Leapers,
many of them; a shoal the like of which she had never come
across. But they were not moving as they should. She sensed
and heard them in the cages but she had never seen anything
like this and couldn't understand that they were enclosed.
The pup moved again and hunger gnawed at Rondo's
stomach. The Leapers were there for the taking. She ad-
vanced slowly, her nose and eyes below the surface, but still
confused by the sheer numbers of silver fish only a few seal's
lengths from her. Had she been more suspicious, moved past
perhaps and settled for the Angler fish a mile or so away, she
might not have been struck down.

It took her at the moment she was about to dive. She was
already tensed, ready to drive forward, and as she was hit,
continued to move, adrenalin surging in her blood and every
Message of The Ages racing through her brain. The bullet
had been light. But it was swift, very swift and bore a soft,
lead tip which first flattened then spread as it impacted
muscle and bone. It was like a fire burning in her, but still
she drove in a shallow dive out into the deeps, a mad chemistry pulsing through every muscle, every sinew, to leave her
limbs oblivious to pain and drive her forward to safety. The
sound of the shot still rang in her ears and grew louder. She
slowed, her body no longer moving in grace and with control
but weaving, curving in her flight. She half rolled onto her
back, curving again then bending and twisting rapidly as
though in pursuit of some close but unseen quarry or
enmeshed in an invisible net, fighting to free herself. Her
limbs no longer moved in unison, but flapped gainlessly and
without control.

She grew dizzy. She was on fire and then encased in ice.

All the pain of every Eye-pecker of the Northlands and all the tortures of the plague were not as great as the pain she felt now. She looked upward, longing for breath, longing for the caress of clean, cooling air.

On the salmon cages in Bay of Otters a man stood up and slung a rifle over his shoulder. He searched with a glass across the surface of Loch Shiel. Seeing nothing, he looked at his watch. "Five minutes," he said to himself. "Must be dead by now".

Rondo hung motionless in the water, her vision blurred and a strange, peaceful slackness shrouding her. Her spirit began to dull then. She was blind and no matter how hard she tried it was impossible to move. She felt the call of sleep and did not fight it for there was nothing left in her, and all the Messages and Lessons of The Ages had faded from her mind. Rondo One-Eye felt her first pup kick before consciousness left her. She slept, then drifted slowly downwards through the deeps, down to the ancient graveyard of her Kind on the dark floor of Loch Shiel.